A FEMINIST POSITION
ON MENTAL HEALTH

A FEMINIST POSITION
ON MENTAL HEALTH

By

MARY BALLOU, Ph.D.

Department of Counseling Psychology
Northeastern University
Boston, Massachusetts

and

NANCY W. GABALAC, M.Ed.

Toledo Society for the Handicapped
Toledo, Ohio

With David Kelley, Ph.D.

CHARLES C THOMAS • PUBLISHER
Springfield • Illinois • U.S.A.

Published and Distributed Throughout the World by
CHARLES C THOMAS • PUBLISHER
2600 South First Street
Springfield, Illinois 62717

© *1985 by* CHARLES C THOMAS • PUBLISHER

ISBN 0-398-05040-6

Library of Congress Catalog Card Number: 84-8495

With THOMAS BOOKS *careful attention is given to all details of manufacturing and
design. It is the Publisher's desire to present books that are satisfactory as to their physical
qualities and artistic possibilities and appropriate for their particular use.* THOMAS
BOOKS *will be true to those laws of quality that assure a good name and good will.*

Printed in the United States of America
Q-R-3

Library of Congress Cataloging in Publication Data

Ballou, Mary B., 1949-
  A feminist position on mental health.

  Bibliography: p.
  Includes index.
  1. Feminist therapy. 2. Women — Mental Health.
3. Women — Psychology. I. Gabalac, Nancy W. II. Kelley,
David. III. Title.
RC489.F45B35 1984   616.89'14'088042   84-8495
ISBN 0-398-0540-6

PREFACE

THIS book is the result of a joint process between the two authors. It has been a complex but wonderful experience involving several aspects clearly parallel to health maintenance, the last phase of the model of feminist therapy presented in the book. We came to both understand and complete our goal, this book, through the effort, ideas and support of one another. Each of our ideas has been enriched by the other, just as our motivation, commitment and enthusiasm have been heightened, rekindled, and sustained by the other.

Our understandings and conceptualizations presented in the book have been influenced by many factors and people. David Kelley's contribution is far greater than the opening historical essay. He demonstrated that men can work with and be helpful to women on their own terms and by their own definitions. His sensitivity to and support of us are an important influence in this book.

Eva Rathgeber's contributions are critical to this book, and her interaction with us epitomize feminist sharing. We employed Eva to check the organization, logic and tone of the book. Her experience in publishing, skill in analysis and politics have greatly influenced the outcome of the book. Her critique of each chapter and the book as a whole has helped significantly. She often caught our ethnocentrism, our tautology, and our class/culture bias. She also helped tremendously with the tone and organization of the book. In a marathon meeting in Boston in the fall of 1983, when her work was finished and the compensation reckoning was at hand, Eva gave us her time and effort. She made her hours, and hours of work, a gift to us. That experience was both touching and humbling for us. In no small way, Eva's gift has shaped this book.

Many other factors less easy to define have also influenced us. Living in American society as women, training in educational institutions, and being employed in mental health service and training settings, have provided many experiences for each of us. Our reflections upon these experiences have certainly influenced this book. Women known to us as friends, feminist colleagues, clients and students, as well as through literature, are represented in this work. And of course both feminist thought and women's psychology, engaged by discussion and reading, have also contributed to our work.

This book, as with any work, has been assisted, shaped and influenced by many people, events, existing literature, and experiences in its joint creation. We and it have been enriched by the gifts and support received.

This book is an analysis of mental health through feminism, an integration of the psychology of women and feminist theory, and an explication of feminist mental health. This book is a beginning in moving the field to the next level of development. We understand our work as the next step in the development of the psychology of women and a feminist analysis of mental health. Our work integrates earlier work, both descriptive and model building, and sets the direction of further development. Hoping to stimulate dialogue, we have pushed the parameters and challenged assumptions not only of traditional mental health, but also of feminist therapy and the psychology of women.

This book is not meant to provide answers, nor is it meant to be an encyclopedia of earlier work. Rather, it is a work which is building upon earlier work, and presents fundamental feminist challenges to traditional mental health and the psychology of women— challenges which hopefully will engender dialogue and further development. In this regard, we do not hide or apologize for this book's politics; rather, we assert it. It is a work which calls for analysis and action and change. The perspective and assumptions we hold are articulated in the text.

The breadth and diversity of areas covered in the text make it potentially useful and relevant for a wide range of readers interested in women. The explications of the harmful adaptation process, with the psychic link between sexism and self image (i.e., ascribed social roles, self denial becoming self hate), while not new, is treated in a systematic manner in this text and is important in understanding women. The psychic link is a concept which is vital for all those who seek to understand women. The analysis and challenges of theory, methodology, and ideology, as well as the current status of feminist therapy and mental health training, are particularly important for academics and researchers. The two chapter presentation of a model for feminist therapy which challenges many traditional assumptions of therapy in contending that interdependent relationships among women are not only necessary but good, and that turning to other women for comfort and validation is critical, are particularly relevant to practitioners. Also vital is the final chapter, dealing with the impact and challenge of feminist social/political action to traditional mental health services.

Feminists, whether trained in mental health or other disciplines, will potentially find the integration and content and historical essay chapters germane. The book, however, is not intended to be separate chapters, relevant to particular groups. It is a whole, each part relating to, influencing, and influenced by each other. History, politics, ideology, and institutionalization cannot be separated from theory, practice and research any more than social roles can be separated from psychological development or social change action from therapeutic aid. Complexity, interaction and evolving consciousness are fundamental to this book and to the developing stage of feminist analysis of mental health.

CONTENTS

A FEMINIST POSITION
ON MENTAL HEALTH

CHAPTER ONE

ROOTS OF MODERN FEMINIST
STRUGGLES

ONLY in the 19th century was the state of western society sufficiently like that of contemporary society to produce a feminist
movement directly linked to today's concerns. By the 19th century,
as an inheritance from the enlightenment, rational analysis combined with scientific orientation was the dominant mode of thought.
From this orientation grew the industrial way of life accompanied by
a bourgeoning urban pattern of existence. All these trends contributed to a broad thrust for popular political representation and
power. The historical position of women in families, work and intellectual life before the 19th century, of course, left a legacy of problems and examples, but little sense of mass movement toward
change. We begin, then, in the 19th century to trace the roots of contemporary trends in the feminist movement.

In the 19th and early 20th centuries, the feminist movement had
the liberal, socialist and radical orientations still discernable today.
What distinguishes such orientations? Liberalism is simply the quest
to change society through moderate means so that the individual can
flourish. Equality of opportunity and equal political rights are two of
liberalism's most fundamental tenets. Socialism goes beyond liberalism as it demands actual equality which, given its analysis of society
by class, can only be achieved through collective rather than individual effort. Socialism also has a revolutionary face which, even when
moderated, retains a millenial aspect.

While both liberal and socialist feminism generated mass political followings, radical feminism was a more intellectual movement looking for the root causes of political patriarchy in the cultural inheritance, in the organization of work, and in sexual roles; to paraphrase a later formulation, the personal as political. It is clear that these categories are artificial. Individual women often moved from one emphasis to another, but collective efforts and organizations tended to be more singular in orientation than did the individuals within them. We will show both the singularity and the overlap that existed historically within the feminist movement.

American liberalism has its roots in the enlightenment ideas that justified the American Revolution and the Republic; in the romantic urges of the New England Transcendentalists who glorified the simple life and the individual in facing the onslaught of industrialism; and in the individualism of Evangelical Protestantism. Politically, its voice rose in the 1830's and 40's on two issues: the horror of slavery, and women's rights. Angelica and Sarah Grimke were early advocates of both these movements; ladies of South Carolina, they had much to say about the immorality of slavery. However, speaking out publicly brought them condemnation from religiously conservative Bostonians, which then led them to question women's place in society. After Angelica's marriage to abolitionist Theodore Weld, both sisters adopted domestic roles, but their battles were taken up by others. In 1840, two American women, Lucretia Mott, a veteran abolitionist, and Elizabeth Cady Stanton, a new bride accompanying her husband, attended the World Anti-Slavery Conference in London. At the Conference, the women faced sexual discrimination and were shunted off to the side of the hall, limited to a passive, listening role. Although William Lloyd Garrison, the most famous American abolitionist, proudly joined them in isolation, the women began to talk about the need for women's rights. Eight years later, Stanton and Mott, joined by another abolitionist, Lucy Stone, organized the Seneca Falls convention to discuss the social problems of women. At the convention, Elizabeth Cady Stanton daringly proposed women's suffrage as a goal. She succeeded in gaining acceptance of the motion by having the ex-slave and then most widely known abolitionist, Frederick North Douglas, speak in its favor. Stanton's vision and leadership were noted by a bored school mistress; Susan B. Anthony. Anthony, having already worked with the prohibition and abolition movements, became Stanton's lifelong partner in the struggle for women's rights.

In their partnership, Anthony proved the better organizer, and a person with statistics and facts at her command; Stanton supplied a greater vision and a finer sense of rhetoric. Their close relationship allowed Anthony to help Stanton in the care of her growing family (four sons and two daughters) and, in this task, they had the further aid of a feminist housekeeper, Amelia Willard. During the 1850's, the two women resolved never to turn down a chance to speak in public, and engaged in the struggle to attain many aspects of personal freedom, women's legal rights, more liberal divorce laws, as well as the right to vote.

In the debates of the 1850's Stanton and Anthony often found support in the broad reform element that included the abolitionists and those coalescing to form the Republican Party. The Civil War, and more particularly the Reconstruction Era, tended to shatter these alliances. In victory, the question of Negro equality and enfranchisement became central for radical Republicans. "It is the Negro's hour" was their slogan, and when Anthony, Stanton, and Sojourner Truth pointed out that half of those Negroes were women, the contradiction didn't concern the male Radical Republicans. Stanton and Anthony withdrew their allegiance to Republicanism and went off in search of new allies. Lucy Stone and other New England feminists clung to the hope of their less-than-honored alliance.

Although women's suffrage remained Stanton's and Anthony's major goal in their search for new alliances, they attempted to work with other reform elements, and their journal, The Revolution (1868-1870), addressed a broad range of women's concerns in its short life. They developed a brief connection with the nascent labor movement which reflected their awareness of America's future. Less to their credit was their fling with the Democratic party which had a racist tinge. The group with which they had the most sustained and fruitful alliance was the growing number of women of middle class origin who now worked as clerks, shopkeepers, teachers, etc. This last group tended to affirm the middle class nature of the suffrage movement.

Throughout the 1870's, the two women spoke and wrote primarily on suffrage. In the 1880's, the issues that separated them from the New England movement had disappeared, and one suffrage organization emerged. About this time, Stanton questioned the limited acceptance of the reform, and began to search for answers. For her, the answer lay in the patriarchal stance of American Christianity, and she began a project of writing a women's Bible as a solution. Thus, while she and Anthony remained friends, it was the latter who continued the major organizational efforts and passed the mantle of leadership to Carrie Chapman Catt. Although Catt had received her organizational training in the broad reform movement of the time, specifically in the Women's Christian Temperance Union (WCTU), she narrowed down the aim of the movement to suffrage. Because of Catt's specific reform emphasis, the organization officially rejected Stanton's work on the women's Bible, even though Stanton remained the group's titular leader.

Eventually, Catt sought an alliance with Woodrow Wilson, even to the extent of supporting World War I, and women's organizations and war work led in 1920 to the attainment of suffrage. One element of the movement, led by Alice Paul, objected to such expediency. Paul, trained in the equally middle class but more tactically militant British movement, preferred a strategy of confrontation. This difference between the leaders and their organizations became apparent after suffrage was achieved. The major suffrage movement headed by Catt evolved into the National League of Women Voters, while Paul organized the much smaller Women's Party which proposed and fought for an Equal Rights Amendment. By focusing narrowly, Catt made suffrage safe but less meaningful. Paul continued the liberal tradition of individual rights but found only a small audience. She did emerge briefly in the 1970's as the elder stateswoman.

The development of the British suffrage and liberal feminist movement often paralleled that of the American movement. The widespread political involvement of women began with the anti-slavery movement and continued with war work (for the Crimean War in the 1860's). Like American women, the British feminists found influential male allies, for example, John Stuart Mill, the great liberal ideologist, who published a remarkable essay at mid-century demanding full equality for women in all areas. (Mill drew directly from the ideas of his wife and daughter, but published alone because his name would produce a greater audience.) In the 1860's, activist women formed a suffragist organization with Millicent Garrett Fawcett, an upper middle class lady, at its head. This organization closely allied itself to the Liberal Party and its general reform attitudes (favoring education and a wider franchise). Early achievements for some women's property rights, and even women taxpayers' (usually widows) right to vote in local elections cemeted some to this Liberal Party alliance, but it gradually became less and less fruitful.

Britain had more militant reformers than the Liberal Party, and out of these ranks came Richard Pankhurst. He was first a Liberal, then a radical, and finally a socialist reformer. His example imbued his wife Emmeline and his daughters, Chrystabel, Sylvia, and Adela, with a sense of action and idealism. After his death, Emmeline entered the reform battles as a free speech advocate, struggling for the rights of the Independent Labor Party. Chrystabel picked up her father's advocacy of women's rights and became active just before the turn of the century with a vaguely socialist feminist group. Chrystabel convinced her mother that women's rights should be their principal activity. In the early 20th century, they formed the Women's Suffrage Political Union (WSPU), at first allied with the Labor Party and then completely independent. What separated the WSPU from the older suffrage group was the fiery oratory and militancy which attracted national attention and the support of some wealthy liberals. Eventually, Emmeline and Chrystabel led a violent agitation for the vote which included window breaking, fires in post boxes, arson of empty public buildings, arrests, hunger strikes which at times resulted in forced feeding, and speeches and mass demonstrations. The younger Pankhurst sisters were not part of the WSPU. Sylvia followed her mother and older sister into suffrage agitation, but did so in the slums of London's East End, organizing poor women around the newspaper, *Worker's Dreadnought*. Agitating, demonstrating, hunger striking, she spoke for suffrage and wider reform, and seemed to compete with her mother and sibling, who excluded her from their organization which drew from the middle class women for membership and financial support. The WSPU played up class differences as part of their rhetoric, pointing out the disfranchisement of educated middle class women, when poor and uneducated working class men had gained the vote. Adela agreed more with Sylvia's broader vision, but she escaped conflict by emigrating to Australia where she continued the family tradition of socialist and feminist agitation.

Like Catt in the United States, though in a more tactically radical fashion, Emmeline and Chrystabel narrowed the focus of their liberal feminist movement to the question of the vote. Also like Catt, they were to use World War I as an opportunity to advance their cause. When the war came, Chrystabel (always the tactician) ordered an end to agitation and instead mobilized women for war work. As a reward came suffrage.

In both nations, suffrage was the symbol for a broader movement, but the symbol required so much effort that it became the end with little further content, and the liberal feminist movement fell upon hard times. The first woman elected to Parliament was the wry Lady Astor, and the Pankhursts drifted far from their origins. Emmeline became a Conservative Party spokesperson; Chrystabel, a Seventh Day Adventist; and even Adela (after much leftist infighting) became an anti-Communist speaker. Only Sylvia stayed true to the socialist ideals, and she became a spokesperson for Ethiopia against Italian fascism. In Britain, only female trade union leaders and socialists such as Beatrice Webb had any idea of which problems should be confronted with women's votes, and they had not been part of the fight for suffrage. In America, Alice Paul and others did have a direction for liberal feminism, but they made little progress.

One aspect of Paul's program, which also briefly became a goal of the WSPU after enfranchisement, was the expansion of women's work alternatives. We have already noted that support for suffrage in America came from middle class working women. Indeed, as early as the mid-19th century, feminists of a liberal bent also focused on the world of female work. In England, these women first looked at the plight of the governess, who was in a family but not really of it. For middle class women, this position was the only respectable one if their own family failed. Feminists saw the need for other avenues, and agitation developed for the establishment of women's schools and for greater career opportunities. America had established examples. Oberlin College, founded in 1833, was the first to be fully open to women, and a few years later Mount Holyoke (1837) was established as a modern academy for women. Somewhat later, British education also moved in this direction. In 1847, the Governesses' Benevolent Institute developed a lecture series to train governesses and other middle class women in modern educational techniques. With this as a basis, Queen's College began a year later.

By 1858, the *English Women's Journal*, devoted to the problems of working women and career opportunities, began in publication. The *Journal* established its own printing cooperative and aided women in business (usually as shopkeepers), as well as encouraging the growth of women's roles in the clerical field and in the teaching and nursing professions. Among the many areas of work, printing was clearly the most discriminatory against women, but also offered the greatest potential for women to become skilled workers. Not only did the English women seek openings in the field, but in America, Stanton and Anthony published their paper through a women's cooperative and attempted to negotiate a place for women with the printers' trade union. All of this was an outgrowth of the liberal feminism movement, but much of its activity was overshadowed by the drive for suffrage. However, these are the historical predecessors of contemporary organizations like NOW which focus on discrimination in employment.

The political milieu of continental Europe did not favor the rise of a liberal feminism. In France, despite the advanced ideas of Condorcet who favored women's equality during the French Revolution and the work of Flora Tristan in the french labor movement in the 1840's, the central conflicts of the 19th century were between socialist and anarchist ideas. The French liberal movement emphasized the dominance of the church, and its focus was on anti-clericalism. Indeed, neglect of women's issues in the 19th century created a climate in which French feminists were not strong enough to win the vote until 1940. The case in Germany was quite different, but again there were few parallels to English speaking nations because socialist feminism came to dominate women's issues in that country.

Contemporary feminist critics of socialism point out that Karl

Marx was a rather stodgy, patriarchal Victorian in family matters who practiced the double standard by keeping mistresses, and that his and socialism's promises of utopia through revolution had borne less than perfect female equality in the socialist countries of the USSR, China, and Cuba, as well as in Eastern Europe. Admittedly, revolution did bring change and progress for women in these countries, but the degree of achievement was no greater than in Western-style democracies, although the starting position may have been worse. These criticisms are valid, but they ignore the fact that the socialist ideology held a historical promise for women as well as the reality of socialist organization for women's issues.

Even before Marx, utopian socialists such as Charles Fourier concentrated on the issue of abuse of women, and from the outset Karl Marx and Frederick Engels saw the position of women as basic to an understanding of the exploitation of people by people and class by class. Engels, in his *Origins of the Family*, argues that the first division of labor was between men and women, with men assuming a domination over women. In their scheme of dialectical, historical materialism, both Engels and Marx saw this original exploitation echoing down through each new system of class exploitation. In their day, this exploitation worked in two ways. First, the family at the working class level became merely a means to exploit the male worker further by using the unpaid labor of the wife and children for his sustenance. At the middle and upper class levels, women were seen as legal prostitutes who had sold themselves as slaves to men in exchange for the material goods which men controlled. Second, when women were forced into the labor market by capitalism, they were allowed only the most degraded, menial, and exploited positions. Marx further noted that as capitalism expanded, more and more women would be forced to work. By this Marxist analysis, all women gained in the revolutionary overthrow of capitalism and the succeeding utopia which abolished all class relations.

While feminist ideas are inherent in socialist ideology, one individual, August Bebel, in *Die Frau und der Socialismus* (Women and Socialism), brought these ideas into sharp focus in 1883. This book became the most widely published and translated work in the Socialist movement with the exception of Marx's *Capital*, and given the density of *Capital*, Bebel's work was probably more widely read and enjoyed. With passion and fire, Bebel carefully analyzed women's position, and used his findings to fill in the Marxist outline. He also suggested the future under socialism:

> The woman of future society is socially and economically independent; she is no longer subject to even a vestige of dominion and exploitation; she is free, the peer of man, mistress of her lot. Her education is the same as that of man...She chooses her occupation on such field as corresponds with her wishes under conditions identical with man's...She joins in studies, enjoyments or social intercourse with either her sisters or with men — as she may please or occasion may serve. In the choice of love, she is, like man, free and unhampered. She woos or is wooed, and chooses the bond from no consideration other than her inclinations....

Furthermore, since property is dead,

> Woman is, accordingly, free, and her children, where she has any, do not impair her freedom; they can only fill all the fuller the cup of her enjoyments and her pleasures in life. Nurses, teachers, female friends, the rising female generations — all these are ready at hand to help the mother when she needs help.[1]

For Bebel, women's position would become equal in all respects, socially, educationally, economically. As indicated, he advocated the abolition of family because it was a means of holding and controlling property. He did allow the free will union of two people for a lifetime if they both so desired. Bebel managed to remain free of sexual stereotypes to a remarkable degree, although a small note creeps in on the rearing of children outside the old family structure. While not mentioned in the quotation, he advocated full political equality to begin immediately. His advocacy meant that German socialism came out for the enfranchisement of women before any liberal women's movement arose. (When liberal women did organize, they feared to press for the vote because it would identify them with socialism.) The courage of his positions was also notable because he wrote when German socialism was illegal and when women's position was reflected by a law that banned them from even attending political meetings (in effect until 1908).

---

[1] Bebel, August: *Woman and Socialism.* New York, Schocken Books, 1971. Reprint of a 1904 edition translated by Daniel DeLeon.

With this theoretical tradition, the German socialist movement was open to women from all levels of society who stressed different aspects of feminism. From the middle class came Clara Zetkin who as a student in Switzerland married an impoverished and consumptive Russian revolutionary Marxist. Because of his illness, she was forced to support them by doing piecework labor, gaining a first hand knowledge of the problems of the poorest women. She later became the leading spokesperson of socialist feminism acting through the journal *Gliechheit* (Equality), which she edited. Also from the middle class was Helen Stocker. Well educated, Stocker considered herself a follower of Neitzche and bent his philosophy of self-fulfillment to expanding the role of women (even married women, which was difficult given the legal patriarchical rights of husbands at that time). From the lower classes came Marie Juchaz, the daughter of a farmer. Sharing household and child rearing tasks with her supportive sister, she agitated for more extensive welfare measures for women. Louise Zietz was the daughter of a handcraft weaver whose income and position was being rapidly undermined in German industrialization. She was forced to work as a piecework cigarette roller at home to help support the family. Later, married to a socialist dockworker, she helped organize unions and associations to improve conditions for this lowest level of the working class (often the only position open to women). Her husband, conscious of the problem and of her talents, actively supported her work. From the opposite end of the social spectrum came Lily Braun (nee vonKretschman) of a noble Prussian family. Braun started as a liberal feminist, but found their positions too polite and their movement incipient. She openly became a socialist and startled audiences with her upper class accent and her Berlin wit, becoming one of socialist feminism's most vibrant and sought-after speakers. Unfortunately, she later became caught up in the nationalist frenzy before World War I and deserted her earlier positions.

While socialist feminism had its origin in Germany and created there an array of militant women leaders and followers, the concepts had international impact. In America, the socialist party had a separate women's organization whose membership was as great, proportionately, as female membership in the German party. (The American party as a whole was smaller than the German, but at the turn of the century it was a mass movement with hundreds of thousands of followers.) Many prominent women, like Frances Willard and Margaret Sanger (who we will discuss below), received training and found support in this American movement. Socialist (although not necessarily Marxist) ideas influenced a whole group of women who agitated both for women's issues and general reform. These included Jane Addams and her Chicago group, some of whom organized the Women's Trade Union League. The League used middle class morality to support the trade union organization of women in the lowest paying jobs. In Britain, Beatrice Webb struggled for many of the same issues as well as making a broad case for reform socialism.

Both liberal feminism and socialist feminism created mass political movements for change; but one got caught up in the drive for the vote and the other, with a more complex analysis, tended to put off reform to the future revolution. Neither answered immediate needs of women, which left room for two other movements, the cult of domesticity and radical feminism. The changes of the 19th century were profound. The industrial revolution rapidly accelerated the movement of work from the home to the factory, department store and eventually agribusiness; new scientific theory produced alarming social ideas. As work shifted, some women began to look nostalgically at former conditions. With formal work and wages separated from the home, monetary power lay more clearly with men, and women's roles seemed diminished. (Actually only some widows had any real economic power, among women, under the pre-industrial system, which is why we use the term nostalgic.) This wistful remembrance of the past produced a women's movement which has been called the cult of domesticity.

The purpose of domesticity was the rest and relaxation of those struggling with the cold, indifferent, larger world. Women's role at home was to love and nurture the husband, rear the children with grace, love and dignity, and aid in the family income by careful management of personal finance and the introduction of domestic economy and efficiency. Initially, this was a women's (although not a feminist) movement, as women trained each other in the new role. One leader was Catherine Beecher, who produced numerous studies of home life and efficiency, and must be ranked among the earliest home economists. She was not alone; cookbooks, manuals on child rearing and books of helpful domestic hints, appeared widely and sold well in not only the United States but in England and on the continent. For example, Mary Wollstonecraft's first books were on child rearing and Isabelle Beeton, and the publishing firm of Clarke, Beeton and Company of England, were the real pioneers of the field. Lest all this sound to the contemporary ear like a form of suburban enslavement, it is well to remember that the aim of this movement and these authors was to insure their dignity and equality, even if limited to a separate role.

The cult of domesticity was often at odds with all varients of feminism, but feminism did make use of some of its trends. If a husband were a drunk, a cad, or simply refused to understand or appreciate the value of women and their domestic creations, then what was the basis of family life? This question raised the legitimacy of divorce and women's rights to a sound family life. Liberal feminists, like Stanton and Anthony, argued for divorce reform (and economic rights in divorce) precisely on such domestic and cultural grounds. (Socialists also fought for divorce but on a somewhat different basis.) Further, if women provided in the home the only solace in society and held the very future, the rearing of children, in their hands, then it was senseless to deny them power in political questions which might affect these fundamental aspects of life. They should vote.

Feminists and those convinced by the cult of domesticity arguments influenced each other on several other issues. The ultimate domestic relationship is sexual. Here also the cult of domesticity developed extreme (if not progressive) approaches. The constant bearing of children not only destroyed the health of many women, but limited the possibility of rearing children well. The solution from these home-oriented women was sexual repression; it was one way of asserting control over their own lives. For some women who argued from the domestic perspective, this view of sexuality was not narrow. They fought the common dual standard in sexual relations, arguing men should be as pure as women. Although prostitution from this viewpoint might seem the ultimate evil, these women sympathized with prostitutes as victims. Much of the activity about prostitutes was rather stodgy "rescue" work, but in the 1860's when England passed a series of Contagious (venereal) Disease Acts which applied only to women (police would determine who was a prostitute and were empowered to force inspection of, and "cure" for, the disease). Josephine Butler led a successful campaign to eliminate the laws on the basis of equal civil liberties for women. Butler clearly identified with all women, even her "most unfortunate sisters."

Finally, feminist concern about home life also helped create two other widespread movements: for prohibition, and protective laws for women workers. Clearly high alcohol consumption has a deleterious effect on home life, especially among the poor. In America, a woman with both feminist and socialist ties, Frances Willard, took up this cause, eventually founding the long standing and at times potent Women's Christian Temperance Union. Concern for the fate of lower class women also was apparent in the fight for protective legislation for women workers. Recognizing the dual role of poor women, as workers and as mothers, women socialists and reformers argued for limitations of hours and work loads for women along with healthier work environments. Socialists hoped that the new conditions would become standard for all workers in an industry, not used as a means to exclude women, but their basic argument for better conditions was the special place of women because of the maternal or future maternal role. To some extent, these arguments contradict each other and the final result was reform that led to exclusion.

While advocates of the cult of domesticity and feminists cooperated on specific campaigns, at its core the cult of domesticity was antithetical to feminism of all kinds. Its basis was essentially biological, that women's bodies suited them for a specific role. As early as the mid 19th century, male opponents of feminism, like the Englishman John Ruskin, had focused on the concept of domesticity as a means of flattering women but suggesting that they stay at home. By the late 19th century, a whole debate on women's biological nature (and limitations) was in progress. Darwin's theories made biological speculation one of the primary modes of late 19th century thought. The resulting Social Darwinism propounded by Herbert Spenser touted male virtues of competition, aggression and domination as creating progress for both the individual and society. A Scottish biologist, Patrick Geddes, suggested these qualities were inherent in the very cells: the male (sperm) aggressive, and the female (ovum) passive, absorbing energy, protecting and creating new life. Geddes' biology was speculative, but he did draw an interesting conclusion: that the female traits really held society together by seeking peace, order, and cooperation. Most feminists object to any biological determination of roles. As early as the 1840's, Stanton and Anthony adopted the costume of Amelia Bloomer because it gave them the same physical freedom as men. (The costume caused such controversy that they dropped it after a few years in the interest of pursuing suffrage.) When males argued against female higher education because of the debilitating effects of menstruation, the feminist movement simply ridiculed them. However, the biological arguments in the late 19th century did lead a few prominent women, like Jane Addams, at least to state a preference for Geddes' arguments. Indeed, Geddes' conclusion, if based on cultural rather than biological grounds, has a modern echo in feminist concepts that abhor the competitive male social structures; arguing that women should not simply become like men, but that men also need liberation from aggressive and overly-competitive milieus.

While the cult of domesticity was an answer to the problems raised by 19th century trends, it had many conservative drawbacks. Some feminists took a sharply different view. These women eventually saw suffrage as too limited an aim, and socialism as not specifically interested in women's problems. They identified the central problem as patriarchal values centered in the family and the roles it prescribed for women. This thought is the core of what we call radical feminism. Radical feminism looked at women working outside the home quite positively and wanted basic changes within the home as well.

Perhaps the clearest demand of radical feminism was for sexual liberation as an individual right. One of the early advocates of this individual freedom was Mary Wollstonecraft in the late 18th century. Wollstonecraft was cut off, by her sex, from her family's modest middle class income. She supported herself as a governess, mistress of a miserable school for girls, and finally as a hack writer and translator. In this last role, she produced a small masterpiece, *Vindication of the Rights of Women* (1790), which argued emotionally (romantically) and logically (in the spirit of enlightenment) for wider, freer roles for women. She could, of course, draw on her own experience for the passion of the book. As a noted author, during the remainder of her life she spoke her ideas. She lived freely, writing political commentary from France during the Revolution, bearing a child out of wedlock, and eventually marrying the famed anarchist, William Goodwin (a marriage shocking to their friends because it defied Goodwin's philosophy). Wollstonecraft died while bearing Goodwin's first child, but he published her letters and journals, which described a rather shocking example to increasingly conservative English society.

Wollstonecraft was not alone in her attitudes. Other women, usually writing to support themselves, by their contemporaries' standards, led disordered lives. The novelist George Elliot was a notorious example, and these ideas were brought to American shores by Frances Wright, a feminist author, lecturer and communal socialist. Indeed, many utopian communities were founded in America in the 1830's and 1840's. Many advocated some variant of free love, that is, love without property consideration and by personal choice. Actual views on sexuality and its place were different for each community. Robert Owen and his son established several communities and generally advocated contraception. The most interesting practice was Kerrenza (sexual stimulation without coitus) which supposedly aroused but then retained sexual energy for other of life's tasks. Some groups, like the Shakers, simply thought that sex stood in the way of honest male-female relations and preached abstinence. Indeed, by the 1870's even radical marriage reformers and feminists like Victoria Woodhull and her sister Tennessee Claflin (a spiritualist as well as a feminist), advocated abstinence, rather than artificial contraception, to space and limit the number of children. They took, however, strong stands against marriage in their weekly newspaper, preaching only "free love" unions. Hence, even though their philosophy closely resembled that drawn from the cult of domesticity, they were seen as a truly shocking pair.

By the turn of the 20th century, the idea of women's sexual nature and sexual desires was widespread. The writings of Woodhull and Claflin, of Edward Carpenter in Britain, all had effect, but the means to more open sexuality, contraception, was still frowned upon. There had been discussion and even pamphlets about birth control as early as the 1820's (the great English liberal, John Stuart Mill, was jailed for such writings), but the modern movement in favor of contraception really began in European and American socialist/anarchist feminist circles. The famed American anarchist, Emma Goldman, openly advocated freedom of sexual enjoyment through contraception. Others, notably Margaret Sanger, coming through socialist circles, took this cause as their critical life's work. Sanger, trained as a nurse, went to Europe to study contraceptive methods practiced by socialist clinics in France. When she returned, she had a medically effective means of birth control that she felt safe to advocate. With some struggle, she helped make contraception a normal, professional aspect of the medical world. Such activity produced a startling change in sexual mores in the 1920's which was to establish a new pattern, unaltered until the 1960's.

A second critical area of interest to radical feminism was the movement of women into the labor force. They supported such a movement and fully understood its negative implications for the future of the home and its domestic functions. In the late 19th and early 20th centuries, Charlotte Perkins Gilman considered these implications. She was well suited to do so, since she had been forced to abandon a stifling marriage at the cost of surrendering her child. Her solution was radical, the abolition of the family work unit as it was known. Basically she borrowed from socialist concepts and saw a trend of mass machine functions replacing housework. Cooking and cleaning would be done by machine on an industrial basis (much in the same way as the manufacture of clothing had become industrial). Child care would be cooperative. The role remaining for the family would be emotional sustenance in the evening hours in a small efficient apartment; with the drudgery gone, there would be love and communication. Gilman misread the future, not envisioning the myriad of household gadgets which would ease women's labor in the home but keep her tied to the house. Her ideas continue to appeal to women as they join the national labor force, but still find themselves burdened with the household tasks and hence a double job.

A final concern of radical feminism surfaced in the late work of Stanton on the *Women's Bible*. As noted earlier, she wondered after 40 years of effort, why there was so little success. In order to explain this dilemma, she focused on the patriarchy of American Christianity, thus starting the search for the basis of male dominance in families and society.

In sum, the roots of feminism in the late 19th and early 20th centuries include liberal, socialist, and radical variants. The liberal root focused on the needs and rights of the individual, including political rights and later financial opportunities. The socialists took a more comprehensive view, placing the plight of women in the economic context. While struggling for many immediate changes, they sought liberation in altering the entire social and economic structure. The radical feminists shared much with the socialists in their broader view of the problems, but focused more on the social rather than the economic structure, particularly the basis of all social structures: the family. The variants of feminism are more apparent in organizations than in individuals; suffrage groups, socialist parties, and reform efforts such as that for birth control have their distinct histories. Individuals like Stanton or Zetkin had ideas and worked in many directions. Others might work in one area, such as Gilman who was mainly a suffrage speaker, but then have important impact in another area, such as Gilman's view of women's economics. Or they might come through one movement to focus on another as Sanger did in coming from socialism to become a leader for birth control.

If the roots of feminism were strong and varied in the early 20th century, why did the movement seem to collapse in the 1920's? The common answer, that the movement became too committed to suffrage and had no other ideas, is too simple. Liberal feminism was caught in a shift of western ideas away from reform. The bloodshed of World War I and the Bolshevik Revolution shattered illusions of easy progress and all Western society underwent a conservative reassessment. Despite this conservative trend, the 1920's was a period of continued change in a feminist direction. For example, in America, birth control was at its peak, but the real change was in social terms. In America, France, and Germany, women continued to pour into the labor market. (In other European countries, returning veterans and economic doldrums limited entry.) In America, women demanded personal freedom from bad marriages as the divorce rate reached new heights, and within or outside of marriage, women's demands for sexual participation and enjoyment reached a new plateau. Taking our roots analogy seriously, this was the slow building of the trunk of the movement.

Growth did slow in the 1930's. Western economic collapse led to fewer women in the work force. The divorce rate fell sharply as the family became an economic necessity, the only real social security. With war production, the usual economic trends returned with women moving rapidly into the work force and even, if temporarily, gaining better places in the job hierarchy. After the war, the divorce rate topped that of the 1920's reflecting a demand by women to end ill-conceived wartime marriages. The trunk was once again growing, but now came a counter attack.

The late 1940's and 1950's were times of immense insecurity. Europe, destroyed by the war, entered into the throes of reconstruction. America feared a return of the economic depression. Furthermore, America now had a great rival in the Soviet Union. Their rivalry threatened ultimate, nuclear destruction. Seeking security, conservatives consciously returned to the myth of the home, and the cult of domesticity returned as a tool to alleviate at least some social tensions. Even popular terminology linked fears of women's activities in the world with other threats. For example, the term "bombshell" referred to a physically attractive, vivacious woman. The containment of women in the home can be linked to the policy of the containment of Russia with the bomb. In response, both the marriage rate and the birth rate rapidly increased; the divorce rate fell below that of the 1920's, but the movement of women into the labor force continued. The trunk was still solid.

The branching of the feminist movement in the late 1950's required only a nudge. It came first in Europe, as the equity created by the establishment of the welfare state didn't quite reach women. Simone de Beauvoir, in her landmark book of the late 1950's, *The Second Sex*, suggested feminist reasons for this failure. Half a decade later, with the example of Black Americans' demands for civil rights, a widespread feminist movement burst out of America. All the variant roots of feminism found healthy branches. Only the cult of domesticity now seemed inherently conservative, rather a malignant offshoot, except for the healthy twig of wages for housework. The Liberal feminist tradition awoke in the demand for the Equal Rights Amendment and in the National Organization of Women's attempt to expand educational and work opportunities for women. Socialist feminists, with their wide economic interpretation, also spoke in theoretical debates. Since greater participation in the labor force has been the most continuous and powerful change affecting women, socialist feminist voices cannot be ignored. Probably the richest growth has come from the root of radical feminism. From Betty Friedan's condemnation of the mind-dulling suburban mystique (the result of the cult of domesticity of the 1950's), to Kate Millet's attack on patriarchical values of western literature, to Mary Daley's search for feminist theology, to numerous women novelists not only describing women's plight but attempting to give them their own fantasy, the culture of male dominance is under attack. Feminists picking up Gilman's ideas and facing social realities have demanded a great extension of collective child care. Finally, the sexual liberation of women continues not only in the demand for abortion rights, but also in the movement to develop ways of life totally independent of men, characterized in lesbian feminism. In sum, the roots established earlier in the century, growing slowly through the changes in society in the intervening years, have helped produce the mature feminism of today.

CHAPTER TWO

THE CURRENT STATUS OF FEMINIST THERAPY

FEMINIST therapy is an exciting, current development that has been emerging over the last decade. As feminists challenged existing views, practices, and values of the mental health profession, so too does feminist therapy challenge the theory, process, and implicit values of traditional therapies. To understand the development of feminist therapy, one must consider the literature, the principles, and process, and the challenges. The juxtaposition of feminism and therapy has given birth to feminist therapy. Its continuing development demands solid consideration of the basic contradictions between feminism and traditional therapy, not just a description of yet another therapeutic technique. This chapter reviews, organizes, and synthesizes the work accomplished thus far in the development and articulation of feminist therapy. Additionally, it identifies directions in need of further exploration. Perhaps because of the newness and diverse development of feminist therapy, clear consensus does not yet exist. In this text, we shall consider feminist therapy to be a therapeutic paradigm based upon, informed by, and guided through feminism.

Feminist therapy is a term which sometimes has been used loosely in literature. It is not a school of therapy as is Gestalt or Reality therapy, for example. In contrast, feminist therapy is an orientation, a conceptual frame of reference based upon a philosophical-value position. In this way it can be likened to other orientations in the field of psychology, such as the behavioral, humanistic, or analytic approaches. However, feminist therapy, or more accurately the feminist orientation to therapy, has a feminist philosophical-value stance. This distinctive philosophical stance has been detailed in many feminist sources, which will be discussed later in the text. The purpose here is to characterize briefly those aspects most germane to the discussion of feminist therapy.

Feminists believe that non-hierarchical egalitarian relationships should exist in human interaction and in institutional settings. They hold that oppressive (non-egalitarian) social structures and relationships have delimited and shaped women's status and often self-delineation. They reject patriarchy and sex/gender role ascriptions. Feminists value consensual decision-making, equal access to power and open role options. They are committed to social, institutional, and personal change toward these values. Additionally, feminists see both instrumental (masculine ascribed) and expressive (feminine ascribed) needs as legitimate and critical, thereby refuting the societal devaluation of the expressive. Finally, feminists contend that the accumulation of knowledge has been controlled by a male hierarchy and the shaping of knowledge has occurred in accordance with male criteria of achievement, performance, and so on, without regard for the ultimate effects on the quality of life or the nature of reality. In other words, the feminist philosophical stance argues that the dominant world view in American society has been shaped by male needs and perceptions. This dominant world view controls the definitions of women, social structures and institutions, as well as thought and value patterns. The feminist philosophical stance contends that male bias permeates and shapes the psychic and social processes in American society.

Carter and Rawlings (1977) have presented several principles which underlie feminist therapy. The three which most directly make the transition from feminist philosophy to feminist therapy are as follows:

First, women as a gender, and with few exceptions as individuals as well, have less social, political and economic power than men. It is this power differential which accounts for the inferior status of women. Second, women's pathology is fundamentally caused by external, not internal sources; it is the social not the personal which primarily accounts for the "illness" of women. Third, women must attain both economic and psychological autonomy.

These principles, along with the previously presented beliefs of feminism, are critical components of the feminist orientation to therapy. And the feminist orientation to therapy, in turn, cannot be understood without a full comprehension of the significance, subtlety, and impact of feminist analysis.

The therapeutic exchange, assumptions about the nature and causation of "mental illness," and the goals of therapy are highly consistent with the philosophical stance in the feminist orientation to therapy. Indeed, this consistency is one of the outstanding characteristics of the feminist orientation.

As yet, there exists no consensual definition of feminist therapy. As the literature reveals, feminist therapy is in an exciting, yet somewhat ambiguous stage of development where questions abound and only a few answers have been agreed upon.

THE LITERATURE

The literature on feminist therapy comes from diverse sources which range from scholarly journals and texts through newsstand magazines such as "Ms." and popular paperbacks, to grassroots publications such as women's newspapers and literature from women's alternative publishers. The various characterizations of feminist therapy derived from these many sources is confusing and sometimes contradictory. However, upon analysis, this literature appears to fall into three fairly distinct types. The following categorical stratagem highlights the diversity, conceptual interaction, and development of the literature on feminist therapy. These three categories are: 1) the radical, 2) the questioning, and 3) the current status, so named by their approaches in the evaluation of feminist therapy.

The Radical

The first category, the radical perspective, is the most revolutionary because it challenges the roots of western thought and the most fundamental concepts of therapy. Some of the scholarship in this category displays elements of the radical therapy of the 60's and 70's, of socialism and non-western cosmological beliefs as a strategy for implementation of human change and helping relationships. Feminism has drawn from, and at the same time transformed, multidisciplinary thought and social histories of thought. Feminist therapy, as presented in the radical perspective, calls for sweeping change in the traditional conception and practice of mental health. The challenges to existing boundaries and the envisionment of new parameters can be seen in works such as those of Rush and Mander (1974), Griffith (1975), and Wycoff (1977).

Rush and Mander (1974) present the idea of the Mind and the Body as a manifestation of the same essence, or at least as being so intricately integrated as to be inseparable. Griffith (1975) analyzes the politics of helping in the context of therapy and mental health, and also looks at the quality and kind of energy involved in the healing process. The ills of rescuing are examined by Wycoff (1977) as she articulates the impact of the helping roles and practices in the current mental health system. Wycoff (1977) also presents a number of feminist therapy alternatives, each of which result in substantially different impacts. Taken together, the works in this category challenge not only traditional methods of therapy and therapeutic process, but also the fundamental assumptions of human helping activities. Importantly, they do this not merely by criticizing the traditional, but by advancing alternatives.

The works in the radical perspective are an important part in the development of feminist therapy. As implied by the term "radical," this perspective does not share the more common assumptions which are regarded as *a priori* by most of the theories, training programs, practitioners, and mental health centers. Indeed, the radical perspective differs strikingly from traditional therapy. In Chapter Three we will return to more extensive discussion of radical feminist challenges and contributions. The point here is that the authors in the radical perspective, through these extreme contentions, serve to provide the distance necessary to engage in fundamental questions.

The Questioning

The questioning literature is the second category in scholarship on feminist therapy. Works in this category have been written by feminists within the mental health professions as they struggle to move in their thinking beyond the traditional models of therapy, theory, practice, and process. On the whole, writing in this category is more within the boundaries of the usual mental health topics and modalities than the writing in the radical perspective. Yet this category is no less exciting in its thoughtful consideration of issues in the development of feminist therapy. The writers are, within the context of their professions, raising important conceptual and practical issues, using the concepts and working definitions of feminist therapy in critiquing traditional mental health orientations and practices, and offering alternative treatment methods. Their work often stems from descriptive personal/professional experience and contrasting analysis.

There are numerous examples of writing within this category. Williams (1976), drawing from her experience in private practice, attempts to characterize the differential process of feminist therapy. Brodsky (1970), from an academic perspective, questions the theory and process of traditional therapy and sets forth some feminist therapy alternatives. Hare-Mustin (1978) critiques family therapy through a feminist therapy analysis. Feminist therapy is presented by Schaffer (1980) as an alternative to traditional sexist[1] therapy in

---

[1] While many have written of sexism, Marilyn Frye's definition communicates well in the context of our work. She has twice defined sexism. It is interesting to see the development of her thought over the eight years separating the two definitions. Clearly, she has expanded her awareness from individual behaviors and attitudes to include the structures controlling the social fabric. Her work, taken together, defines well our intended meaning of sexism. Sexism must be understood as including both the actions and attitudes of individuals as well as the shaping and enabling social fabric and economic structures of the culture.

The term sexist in its core and perhaps most fundamental meaning is a term which characterizes anything whatever which creates, constitutes, promotes or exploits any irrelevant or impertinent marking of the distinction between the sexes. (Frye in *Male Chauvinism—A Conceptual Analysis, Philosophy and Sex*, 1975.)

However, in 1983, she concludes an essay:

The term 'sexist' characterizes cultural and economic structures which create and enforce the elaborate and rigid patterns of sex-marking and sex-announcing which divide the species, along lines of sex, into dominators and subordinates. Individual acts and practices are sexist which reinforce and support those structures, either as culture or as shapes taken on by the enculturated animals. Resistance to sexism is that which undermines those structures by social and political actions and by projects of reconstruction and revision of ourselves. (Frye, *Sexism*, in *The Politics of Reality; Essays in Feminist Theory*, 1983.)

a text concerning sex-role issues in clinical practice. Finally, Fishel (1979) and Seiden (1976) describe feminist therapy, offering it as a valid alternative model to traditional therapy, and identifying unique features in theory and process.

In this category, writing is essentially representative of thoughtful professionals who are confronting traditional therapy by raising questions, drawing characterizations and setting tentative alternative directions. This work is important for a number of reasons. It represents: (1) important steps in the development of a feminist orientation to therapy; (2) the establishment and demonstration of effective feminist treatment and analysis; and (3) an assertion of feminist therapy as a legitimate force. Later in this chapter we will discuss further some of the ways this category is limited, particularly with respect to its neatly exclusive focus on sex roles. However, it has and continues to be an important aspect of feminist therapy's development, especially in its announcement of feminist therapy within mental health professions.

The Current Status

The third category, the current status, comprises those works describing the state of feminist therapy thinking during the past few years. These works clearly identify the principles of the feminist orientation and show examples of their effective use in clinical practice. Implications for research and theory are also present. In this category, Carter and Rawlings (1977), Gilbert (1980), Sturdivant (1980), Schaef (1981) and Greenspan (1983) offer the best developed statements of feminist therapy. Carter and Rawlings (1977) present text chapters on theory, process, practice, alternative feminist treatments, and a discussion of values and feminism. Gilbert's work (1980) on feminist therapy is in a text by Brodsky and Hare-Mustin (1980) which reviews germane research and identifies directions for further investigation. Sturdivant (1980) has written *Therapy with Women, A Feminist Philosophy of Treatment,* which contains a most thorough integration of earlier work on feminist therapy. Her work is an analysis of the systematic effects of application of liberal feminism to psychotherapy. In her discussion, assuming an essentially humanistic basis, she covers assumption of human nature, pathology and symptoms, technique and sex role bias. The work also contains explicit principles and practices of feminist therapy. Schaef's work *Women's Reality* (1981), also from a liberal feminist tradition, is directed as stated by the subtitle, *an emerging female system in the white male society*, to a more general description of women's existence and needed therapeutic facilitation. Schaef, without the academic structure of Sturdivant, describes some of the forces shaping women's experience in contemporary American culture. The value of her work is a description of the white male power system with contrasting description of a female system, and attention to helping women see and negotiate the conflicts. Unlike Sturdivant, she does not offer a rather systematic analysis of traditional psychotherapy's assumptions and an articulation of feminist therapy. Both taken together offer a comprehensive statement of the current status of a liberal feminist view of feminist therapy.

Greenspan's book, *A New Approach to Woman and Therapy* (1983), is the first American statement of a socialist feminist view of feminist therapy. The English author, Mitchell has analyzed psychoanalysis from a socialistic feminist perspective, and both Tennov and Wycoff, though using predominantly a radical feminist perspective, do use some elements of socialistic feminism in critiquing psychotherapy. However, Greenspan offers a consistent, if couched, socialist feminist statement of feminist therapy. Drawing from her own training and practice experience, as well as collaborative discussions with other feminist therapists, Greenspan has written a book which characterizes feminist therapy. In an unsystematic but wonderfully poignant manner, she addresses traditional psychotherapeutic assumptions, myths, procedures, and sexist practices, while contrasting a feminist approach. Her critique is astute and her description of her socialist feminist approach powerful and captivating. The real strength of this text is Greenspan's illustration of feminist therapy as used with clients, both in conceptualization of their "pathology" and in therapeutic relations and interventions.

The current status category of literature illustrates both the progress of efforts to develop feminist therapy and the diversity in feminist emphases which currently exists. These emphases presented in Chapter One will be discussed more fully in Chapter Three. The current writings in feminist therapy do reflect a certain narrowness.

None of the writers engage topics raised by the radical perspective: spirituality, energy, and healing for example, and they do not engage basic feminist emphases' differences, limits and strengths, or their integration. With the exception of Sturdivant, each presents her own understandings and positions without reference to the others. Clearly, further development and integration is needed. Nevertheless, the works which have been cited are solid statements of the current status of the feminist orientation to therapy.

The three categories which have been identified clarify the developmental process of feminist therapy. The first one illustrates the early radical work of the women's movement and its influence upon feminist mental health professionals in their attention to an initial definition of a feminist orientation to therapy. The second category focuses upon actual use in therapy, upon analysis of other modes of therapy through the feminist perspective, and includes formal communication to the mental health professions. Finally, the current status category articulates a set of principles supported by considerable documentation.

This review of the literature focuses narrowly upon works representing feminist therapy. The development of feminist therapy, however, has been influenced by numerous events as well as by works of feminist scholarship. Diverse activities of the women's movement, general feminist scholarship, and works in psychology such as Chesler's *Women and Madness* (1972), an expose of women's treatment in mental health, Weisstein's *Kinder, Küche, Kirche* (1970), a critique of sexism in psychological research and theory, Brodsky's (1970) essay on C-R groups, and Bardwick's (1971) continuing work on sex differences, as well as other studies such as Spence's (1978) articulation of sex roles, and Broverman, Broverman, Clarkson, Krantz, and Vogel (1970) were important influences. Additionally, the theory and practice of traditional psychotherapy itself has provided strong impetus for feminist therapy. The genesis of feminist therapy is many factored. Professional mental health practitioners and academics, as well as laywomen have contributed to its development.

This review is limited to the literature specifically upon feminist therapy. The developmental perspective is not strictly chronological. Rather, the categories attempt to reflect feminist therapy's richness and diversity. The multifactor influence in the development of feminist therapy gives depth and strength; yet it also results in conflicts. The conflicts serve to spur on development. This process is strong and important, but confusing when analyzed without a developmental perspective.

While the categorical schema demonstrates developmental patterns, it does not attend to the current definition. In the next section, selected aspects of the content of feminist therapy are discussed, and points of consensus and areas of non-consensus are identified. Carter and Rawlings, Gilbert, and Sturdivant each present comprehensive treatments of feminist therapy. The reader is encouraged to pursue their works. The purpose in this section is to illustrate through selected discussion the agreement, debate and further directions of feminist therapy.

CONTENT OF FEMINIST THERAPY

Consensus

As feminist therapy has become more highly developed, a number of dimensions, i.e., principle, practice, and process, have become consensual. The first of these is that feminist therapy is different from non-sexist counseling (Carter and Rawlings, 1977). Non-sexist counseling seeks to treat clients as human beings and actively to refute sex ascriptions in theory and in practice, that is, in options offered to the client and in the values espoused by the therapist. Feminist therapy, while incorporating these goals, moves further in several areas. The essence of the difference lies in the philosophical tenets of feminist therapy. Feminist therapy, as opposed to non-sexist therapy, is critically concerned with the pursuit of social action, with the implementation of changes in institutional sexism and in the sexist social fabric. It demands the analysis of sex roles, the changing of traditional sexist, restrictive role options in women's lives, and the promotion of egalitarian support relationships among women. Feminist therapy places value on being a woman and is concerned with the nature and quality of women's lives. Through a growth and development model, it sees women as being potentially autonomous and claiming personal and social power.

Feminist therapy holds that it is social/economic/political conditions and the sexist attitudes and beliefs generated by them, not internal personality structures, which are the main source of difficulty for women. It argues that women need to understand the profound effect external factors have on them, and work to change the actual external forces as well as the impact they have had upon women as a category, and upon themselves as individuals. Indeed, one of the most important goals of feminist therapy as Moskol (1977) points out, is to assist the client in gaining her personal/social power. Numerous characteristically feminist therapeutic techniques are embodied in feminist therapy. Sex-role analysis, consciousness raising groups, support from other aware women, presentation of choices in lifestyles and values are among these techniques.

Feminist therapy holds that traditional systems of psychotherapy are in serious error which stems from traditional assumptions about women. Therefore, research paradigms, personality theory, clinical practices (i.e., testing, diagnosis, and therapist-patient relationships) are all suspect. Testing and diagnostic labels ordinarily are not used in feminist therapy. The feminist orientation to therapy is eclectic, endorsing theoretical positions which postulate external factors as causative in the client's problems, as well as those which lead the client to an eventual position of self choice. The client's strengths rather than her weaknesses are emphasized. Weaknesses are attended to, but with the assumption that helplessness was a learned response, distress is a reasonable and perhaps adaptive response to hostility and oppression, and the client's environment has retarded her development. The goal is to build skills for coping and creating, to develop astute social analysis, and sophisticated consideration of the potential consequences of change.

An egalitarian relationship between the therapist and client is demanded by feminist therapy. This is characterized by one person (the therapist) having more accessible experience and analysis than the other (the client). The client, however, is every bit as valuable and worthwhile. Further features of the egalitarian relationship are the assumptions that client verbalization is valid, not defensive or unconscious symbolism; all information about the client (case notes, earlier diagnoses, reports, etc.) can be shared with the client; and

open communication of the therapist's values and beliefs occur (Carter and Rawlings, 1977). This overall attitude is characterized by
the facilitation of client self-understanding and the development of
skills through a shared process of learning, which includes reading
and discussion of the clients outside life activities and participation
in relevant women's community events. The assumption that an expert can change the patient solely through access to greater wisdom
and knowledge is rejected. Contracts, clear verbal agreements,
either formal or informal, are made which clearly state the goals and
actions of all parties concerned.

The feminist therapist values women and acknowledges the
necessity of support and skill building, as well as the exploration of
options in thinking and living. Behavioral components of this position are seen in self-disclosure, role-modeling, cognitive restructuring, and the ready use of extra-therapeutic resources. The
feminist therapist uses self-disclosure within the counseling relationship, arguing that self-disclosure is not only consistent with the egalitarian relationship, but also serves to enhance the development of
client awareness of the experience of being female, an experience
consisting of self-abasement and discrimination, as well as struggles
to gain personal and social power. Role-modeling is an important
part of the process. In feminist therapy, overt use is made of the person, experience, behaviors, and attitudes of the therapist. The goal
is not to have the client become just like the therapist, but rather to
set an example of a competent woman dealing effectively with her
life. The therapist consciously sets one pattern, but encourages the
client also to experience other patterns of effective coping. The
therapist recognizes change as a many faceted process, and makes
extensive use of community resources external to the therapeutic relationships. Women's support groups, consciousness raising activities, community action groups, social and legal aid services, and
reading are only a sampling of the resources frequently encouraged.

Feminist therapy also attends to the affective. Indeed, feelings
can be as political as thoughts and actions. The client's feelings hold
importance, yet while the therapy is supportive and accepting of
women, it also is confrontive. Client readiness is a critical aspect.
While nurturance is characteristic of the relationship, over long dependence is not tolerated. To allow dependence only replicates the

traditional status of women. Working through dependence in the therapeutic relationship enhances a client's ability to become more aware of and change dependent statuses elsewhere in her life. As client readiness for change is approached, the overt expectation for movement toward autonomy is verbalized and supported. Empathic responses and caring confrontations are both part of the process of feminist therapy.

Sex role analyses (Carter and Rawlings, 1977) is also a strong part of the exchange. The therapist facilitates the client's ability to understand, both generally and personally, the existence and impact of cultural conditioning and biased social/economic/cultural structures. Aside from sex role analysis which is unique to feminist therapy, any number of other therapeutic techniques are used as appropriate to the situation, the client's needs and readiness, the therapist's skills, and feminist goals. For example, the therapy might employ reflection of feelings, Gestalt exercises, behavioral strategies, body work, interpretation, dream analysis, relaxation, cognitive restructuring, etc.

Validation of the client's experience and personal knowledge is yet another critical aspect of feminist therapy stemming from its theoretical position. It is argued that in a sexist society, subtle and obvious messages abound which communicate to women that they have little power and authority. Interpersonal relations, employment situations, social role expectations, and even parenting frequently contain similar oppressive or restrictive messages for women. In opposition to this, feminist therapy validates women. It seeks to authorize the individual woman; it points out the erroneous messages and their impact upon the individual woman through analysis. Fishel (1979) says, "...the client is viewed as her own best authority, applauded for being a survivor in a hostile environment." The woman is then challenged to engage in the assumption of power and authority for herself. Her own experience, thoughts, words, and intuitions are validated and authorized.

Frequently, personal validation is a new experience and a profound insight for women clients. It often takes time to learn the necessary skills and behavior for the maintenance of this belief, and usually powerful emotions are generated with the onset of and adjustment to this insight. Feminist therapy validates the woman's experience and sees a significant part of the therapy as assisting the client to gain the full experience of being authorized as well as to acquire the necessary skills to claim her power.

Related closely to validation are a gamut of powerful feelings which are not often in conscious awareness prior to validation; rather, they are reflected in physical ailments, self-doubt, depression, and so on. Anger, guilt, rage, pride, joy, determination, and other intense affective states are expected in the process of feminist therapy. Awareness, acceptance, and then constructive use of the affective states are all part of this process. Other survival and growth skills, such as the construction of support systems, self-nurturance, assertiveness, and tactical awareness are developed in keeping with the client's readiness. Indeed, it seems there is an implicit agreement that feminist therapy, without blaming the victim, develops needed skills, restructures cognitions, teaches the meeting and constructive expression of affective needs, and expands the life options for women. Central to these tasks is the self-validation of women's experience and the authorization of the struggle for change.

Feminist therapy is delightfully eclectic in its functioning. It shares some similar features with other therapies; for example, some change strategies, core facilitative conditions, and a tendency to focus attention on both cognitive and affective domains. Two in particular, the contract and the critical questioning of established norms are at least superficially similar to behavior and radical therapies. Feminist therapy, however, has its own interpretations and unique analysis of many of the similar features. There are also a number of unique features, such as sex role analysis, acceptance of eclectic use of change strategies consistent with overt values, focus upon personal and social and political aspects of the client specifically and women generally, and the emphasis on egalitarian relationships. Feminist therapy has a solid and still developing theoretical position, a set of clearly articulated basic principles, and a process which stems from the former and adheres to the latter.

Non-Consensus

There are several areas of apparent disagreement in the works on feminist therapy. Perhaps the most striking area of conflict relates to the kinds of feminist positions held. As discussed in Freeman's analysis of feminism (1974), and in Chapter One, the liberal, social, and radical categories are employed here as an explanatory and reference mechanisms. The underlying philosophical and political stance is usually not made explicit in the literature on feminist therapy. With few exceptions, it appears that most academic feminist therapists are implicitly adhering to liberal feminism: that is, the emphasis in their writings is upon two areas. One is the effects of external factors on the development, growth, and mental health of women (e.g., specific sex role issues). There is also emphasis on the reactions to sexist traditional practices with non-sexist constructs in theory, research, treatment methods, and therapeutic exchange. In liberal feminism, little attention is given to institutional sexism, implementation of strategies for cultural change, and development of methods for effective social action. Nor is there emphasis on the implementation of fundamental change in the social/political/economic structure. Finally, liberal feminism does not deal with non-ordinary or extraordinary phenomena (e.g., spirituality, healing energy, and intuition), nor life options (e.g., collaborative living and collective economic structures). These elements are beyond the scope of liberal feminism, falling instead into social and radical feminism.

The literature suggests that non-academic feminist therapists are more likely to hold radical, cultural, and social feminist positions. In contrast, academic feminist therapists appear more likely to hold liberal positions. There may well be several factors influencing this phenomenon, making it only an apparent dichotomy. For example, the politics of publishing could be one cause. Academic journals in mental health are notoriously conservative. It may be that publication demands force academic feminists to publish in journals unwilling to accept other than liberal feminist positions, while less conservative but non-academic presses allow more diversity. Another factor may be the development of a dichotomy within each author, as the more radical thoughts conflict with the more attainable and less threatening wishes to remediate but maintain the status quo. Then, too, the application of feminism to therapy, as Tennov (1973) points out, engenders certain conflicts, particularly between the individual focus of therapy and the social and cultural focus of feminists. Liberal feminism, because of its restricted focus on sex roles and their discriminatory ascription, is the closest of the feminist positions to this difficult integration. Whether the dichotomy is apparent or real, potential conflict results from the types of feminism underlying feminist therapy.

An analysis of the conflicts resulting from different theoretical positions underlying feminist therapy reveals that there are several direct implications for feminist therapy. For instance, some feminist therapists believe that specific issue social/political action, such as work for the provision of day care, abortions rights, supporting women's alternative services or passage of the Equal Rights Amendment, is an important part of the therapeutic process for the client and a role requirement for a feminist therapist. Other feminist therapists do not hold this belief. Another example is the divergence in commitment to change in the political/economic system. Some feminist therapists believe that an essential part of therapy is commitment to understand and to change cultural norms, institutional sexism, and the social/political/economic system, as well as to work with the individual client and her needs. Yet other feminist therapists believe that the focus should be restricted to dealing with changing sex role ascriptions and their effect upon women. Both activist examples show clearly the divergence in belief and functioning resulting from different philosophical feminist positions underlying feminist therapy. Already there are differences in the literature; for example, Carter and Rawlings (1977) versus Williams (1976) or Greenspan (1983) versus Schaef (1981). This fundamental conflict will become more pronounced as feminist therapy develops more fully.

There is also debate centering around personality theory. Some feminist therapists seem to use traditional personality theory and its practice implications, modified to better fit women's experience. Dinnerstien's adaptation of object relationship theory (1977) is one example. Another would be the humanistic theory and applications of Sturdivant, and Wycoff's use of a transaction analysis formulation. However, other feminist therapists seem to ignore the question of personality theory altogether, as for example Schaef in her focus against the "white male system," or Lerman, who simply asserts that psychodynamic concepts of transference and counter transference in the therapeutic relationship are wrong. Still other feminist therapists

take the question of personality theory and its implications for therapeutic practice quite seriously. Baker-Miller (1976) and Gilligan
(1982) are two examples of feminists deeply engaged in building
theory which stems from women's experience and values. Greenspan
is yet another example of a feminist therapist who is not simply
adapting traditional theory in order to better fit women, nor merely
reacting against traditional procedures. Greenspan, drawing from
her own experience, is articulating feminist practice procedures and
conceptualizations, if not theory. This question of theory is a significant one, and currently very much in focus within feminist therapy's
development. We will discuss this further in Chapter Three.

Another area of disagreement in feminist therapy concerns who
should practice feminist therapy. This question has four aspects: (1)
Who is a feminist therapist? (2) Should males practice it? (3) Should
we adhere to traditional qualification requirements (licensure/
certification)? and (4) How should education and training occur? At
present each of these is an open question. Conflict regarding male
practitioners already exists. Most of the literature sidesteps this issue, either by not mentioning it (Williams, 1976; Lerman, 1976;
Greenspan, 1983) or by giving it only casual attention (Brodsky,
1975; Schaef, 1981; Gilbert, 1980; Sturdivant, 1980; Carter and
Rawlings, 1977). Gilbert raises the question of who is a feminist
therapist, delineating the difficulties in defining suitable criteria.
The professional/non-professional practitioner and the education/
training questions have not yet emerged as conflicting issues in literature. However, in the network of feminist therapists, they are very
much present. It can be predicted with some assurance that these
territorial issues will become central in later stages of the field's developmental process. Moreover, if feminist therapy follows a similar
pattern to that of the current growth of feminism and the Women's
Movement, other issues will arise which relate to women attending
to and accepting a variety of life options. Already the literature is
demonstrating diversity in these areas.

The literature which represents the current status of feminist
therapy has yet to engage in discussion of some of the issues that exist in the larger context of feminism. For example, while Griffith
(1975) writes of women and healing, and Rush and Mander (1974)
discuss the need for female mind/body integration, the writers in the

current status category of feminist therapy have not examined them. Similarly, radical feminists are exploring spirituality, psychic phenomena, and unity with nature; yet feminist therapists are not contributing to these discussions within the therapeutic domain. The literature is silent also with regard to the variety of life options within the women's community, including prostitution, sadomasochism, alternative communities, lesbianism, and radical political action. The exclusion and inclusion of specific dimensions of women's experience is a latent issue for feminist therapy. Certainly these dimensions are problematic as has been demonstrated within the Women's Movement. However, the nature, parameters, and value of all aspects of women's experience demand the attention of feminist therapy. Eventually, either these aspects or their exclusion will become issues for feminist therapy. Certainly other areas (e.g., class, race, and culture, as well as therapist/client ethics) are of critical importance in feminist analysis, and will become focal issues in the future development of the field. Attention, however, is turned now to the final two areas of disagreement in the current stage of feminist therapy: (1) With whom should feminist therapy be used? and (2) What happens after therapy?

Most traditional forms of therapy tend to be in concert with social norms, and to reinforce behaviors and life choices consistent with the dominant cultural expectations. Thus, aside from the stigma of seeking therapy and the initial inculcation to the psychological set, the therapeutic exchange and the goals and outcomes of therapy are quite consistent with those of the larger society. There is little conflict; indeed, most traditional therapy seeks to adjust the patient to society. This is not the case with feminist therapy and leads to at least two important questions.

With whom should feminist therapy be used, is a complex question involving at least five distinct but related subissues. The literature varies in its attention to the question and its subissues.

The first subissue involves whether some women are too disturbed, damaged, developmentally deficient, or psychiatrically impaired to profit from feminist therapy. The literature does not address this issue. However, the position taken here is that some women have "pathology" which is too severe to be dealt with through feminist therapy. For example, a woman who behaves in ways characterized as chronic schizophrenia with marked thought disorder, or moderate mental retardation, would be inappropriate for feminist therapy. There are limits to the range of its applicability. Feminist therapy requires a level of reciprocal relationship (Kell and Mueller, 1966), although this is not to say that feminist therapy is irrelevant in the treatment of such clients. In such cases, feminist therapy has a significant place, but not in psychotherapy with the client. Feminist therapy's unique contribution concerning the genesis of pathology (e.g., external forces and sex role ascriptions) should serve a critical role in the understanding of pathology, and should underlie the treatment, planning and programs in direct service. Feminist positions, coupled with more traditional orientations to treatment and causative factors, will enhance the service given and understanding of women with severe pathology.

Another subissue involves the use of feminist therapy with a traditional woman who is sexist in her belief system. Lerman (1976) and Williams (1976) indirectly imply that feminist therapists always use feminist therapy. Carter and Rawlings (1977) state that non-sexist therapy should always be used while feminist therapy should be used with women who are sufficiently aware. There is a significant question here. Is feminist therapy, or at least those therapies that are non-sexist, to be imposed as sexist therapies now are? In order to fully consider this issue, two further questions must be considered: those of client choice and therapist values. Complex sets of ideas are involved. It is little wonder that the literature does not deal with the issue directly.

At a naive level, certainly clients ought to have a choice. Yet free choice is not given, for without valid information and real options, there can be no free choice (Argyris, 1970). Feminists contend that within the context of a sexist society, women have no free choice since valid information does not generally exist. Indeed, one purpose of feminist therapy is to provide awareness and information of perspectives and options different from dominant sexist orientations. In short, the feminist position is that social conditioning and the controlling external factors obviate free choice. Further, until women are made aware of alternative understanding and options (raised consciousness), there is no real free choice.

Therapists ought to be consistent with their own values and yet not impose these upon the client. However, this is only possible when there is no conflict between the values of the client and the therapist, or when imposition of value injunctions are given only lip service, amounting to being ignored. All therapies impose certain conceptualization and values.

Often in traditional therapies, the therapist's beliefs are essentially consistent with the dominant culture and the adjustment wishes of the client. This is not so in feminist therapy. However, it is apparent that there is an inherent contradiction in the therapist being consistent with her own values, yet not imposing them upon the client. This is perhaps the strongest argument for the conclusion of a pretherapeutic agreement in feminist therapy. Feminist therapists have very clear demands for the first interview which precedes the theapeutic agreement. In the first contact under normal circumstances, the therapist articulates her own values and methods of working in therapy. She helps the client to identify the concerns which have brought her to therapy and her reactions to the values and methods which the therapist has articulated. Conflicts are identified and discussed. If there is no resolution of the conflict, the client is referred to another therapist or service provider. However, unlike in other therapies, feminist therapists articulate them and actively assist the client to consider conflict in belief systems.

Lerman, in a 1976 article, considers the question, "Does Feminist Therapy make Feminists of its Clients?" She concludes that the goal is not to produce feminist clients but rather to assist the client to increase her knowledge of external forces, including the overt and insidious power of sex role stereotypes and controlling external factors. The goal is also to increase the client's awareness of options.

A final area of disagreement to be discussed in the current status of feminist therapy is what happens to the client after conclusion of feminist therapy. Williams (1976) implies that the client, after having increased her awareness, resolved her conflicts, and learned a set of new skills necessary for maintaining her choices, simply terminate therapy. Two inferences are made from Wycoff (1977). First, the women who struggled and worked together in groups during therapy will continue to support one another after therapy. Second, after therapy the women will continue contacts with the larger women's network. Brodsky (1975), Carter and Rawlings (1977), Gilbert (1980), Lerman (1976), and Sturdivant (1980) do not deal directly with this issue, nor can inferences from their work be made with any surety.

The issue of what happens to a woman after feminist therapy is concluded is an important one. Feminist therapy often is in conflict with the norms of the dominant culture, and frequently places a woman in conflict with the usual supports and reward structures in her life and society. The issue has not been covered adequately in the extant literature; Williams (1976) position is unrealistic, Wycoff (1977) hints of dependency, and those who do not attend to the issue are missing a significant aspect. A current shortcoming of feminist therapy is the lack of sophisticated consideration of re-entry (transfer of learning) to the dominant culture from feminist therapy.

It seems that feminist therapy frequently tends to develop in its clients a need for continued feminist activities and support. This, of course, is mediated by the type and depth of the client's concern. Great variability would be expected among clients. For example, a client focusing primarily upon relationship issues involving sharing of home maintenance tasks with a willing partner, the issue would be mild to nonexistent. For a client dealing with sexual identity or professional development concerns, the issue would become more significant.

Several views of the need for continued feminist activity are possible. The basic concern is dependency. Within a traditional therapeutic context, dependency is seen somewhat negatively. Dependency in a client, whether in some area of their life or upon the therapist, is recognized as a dynamic, but one to be changed to independence.

The independent person is individualistic, able to meet her own needs as well as give priority to herself and her own commitments to goals. Traditional therapy would tend to view the continued need for feminist activities as dependency. Non-sexist therapy would see the continuation of client participation in feminist activities as appropriate as long as it were an evaluated and free choice on the part of the client. Feminist therapy analysis would argue that the need is real, valid, and necessary given the external social/economic factors: the oppression of women within the dominant culture. Feminist activities, therefore, offer an environment where women can feel their own worth and be supported. In fact, the feminist activities and community offer an alternative reality. Further, the argument would refute the attitude about dependency. Shepard's view of dependence, independence, and interdependence (1964) is relevant here.

Dependence probably is a necessary developmental need through which one grows. Independence is a mythical goal of the dominant culture. The image of the strong, separate, self-directed, autonomous individual is not useful in group interaction (Shepard, 1964), nor possible in a culture in which community is a desired goal (feminism). Interdependence, in the context of this discussion, would mean personally defined and competent people committed to group benefit as well as personal benefit (Shepard, 1964), or to creating a supportive community for women. Interdependence is necessary for survival within the dominant culture and is perhaps a better vision, certainly a more realistic one, than independence with its individualism, self-priority, and separatism. Interdependence rather than independence then, would be the overt goal of feminism. The feminist analysis calls for recasting of the concepts. It posits that the continuing need for feminist activities, though not feminist therapy, is appropriate for interdependence in the community of women.

Often in the course of therapy, the use of events external to the therapeutic exchange (either individual or group) involves women's activities. These activities might include reading women's movement literature, participation in social action task groups or consciousness raising and musical events, shopping in collective stores, eating in collective restaurants, attending poetry readings, all of which are part of the alternative social and economic women's culture. Important insight, understanding, and experience can be gained from these activities. The sense of being a woman and the definably different nature of these activities is critical to the development of women's consciousness. The supportive, unique experience of participating in the women's community often continues after the therapy is completed. During therapy, exploration of women's resources and groups may have been used. The continuing involvement with the women's community is not seen as a continuation of therapy. The women's community, offering an affirming and supportive alternative social network, is significantly distinct from the dominant culture.

There are important issues still to be faced in feminist therapy. These include the concept of transfer of learning and re-entry: the shifting of learning, from feminist therapy and experience within the women's community, to life in the dominant culture; re-entry from a feminist environment to the sexist situations offered in the dominant culture. This issue is not unique to feminist therapy. Transferred learning problems are shared by National Training Labs, therapeutic communities, specialized institutes (Gestault, Rational Emotive, Primal, etc.), and intensive kinds of individual therapies (e.g., psychoanalysis). The National Training Labs have moved some distance in attempting to address this issue. Feminist therapy has yet to do so.

SUMMARY

Although there are many areas of consensus in feminist therapy, there are a number of points of disagreement as well. Beyond this there are some issues which have not yet been considered in the literature. Feminist therapy currently is in a developmental process and being developed from divergent positions. The process is exciting and rich, and will result in an orientation to therapy reflective not of one person's mind, but of many minds addressing important concerns and issues through actual experience. Nor are the influencing elements narrow in scope. The academic disciplines and areas of human experience intrinsic to feminist therapy are numerous. Feminist therapy has no superstars, nor is it bound by narrow disciplines.

Two issues stand out as current limits in the development of feminist therapy. The first is valid information. Feminist therapy holds that real choice can come only from valid information and genuine options. Yet the question remains, does feminist therapy provide information any more valid than that of the dominant, sexist culture? A feminist would answer, "Of course," while a non-feminist would say, "Of course not." But the point is larger than feminist or non-feminist belief systems. Feminist views have been ignored, censored, or oppressed by the dominant trends in society. They should be thoroughly considered. But confronting one perspective with another does not necessarily yield valid data. Data stemming from analysis, predicated upon one belief system or another, whether articulated or not, are biased. Valid data transcend imposed biases. If it is possible to achieve valid data, and some would argue that it is not, it will come only through a confrontation of underlying values, methodologies, and their shaping and controlling effects on information falsely held out as objective or right.

The second current limit of feminist therapy is the issue of reentry or transfer of learning. Some women, after feminist therapy, will choose options which will keep them primarily within the women's community thereby not experiencing this limit. Others, however, will choose relationships, vocational and avocational options within the dominant culture, and will face this issue directly. Feminist therapy also must face this issue.

This chapter has defined feminist therapy as an orientation to therapy, resulting in a large part from the now historical feminist challenge to mental health. Within this context, three distinct categories have been identified in the multi-source literature of feminist therapy. These categories, the radical, the questioning, and the current status were described. Attention was focused on an integrative analysis of the points of consensus and non-consensus regarding the theory, process, and practice of feminist therapy. Finally, selected issues already existent, and issues predictable by feminism within the women's movement, were identified and discussed.

The mainstream of more traditional researchers, theoreticians, and practitioners has not, as yet, given much attention to feminist therapy. Certainly feminist theory and feminist therapy pose important challenges to the mainstream. The organization and synthesis of the feminist orientation to therapy presented in this chapter and its identification of unresolved issues certainly provides focus for further development of feminist therapy. Chapter Three sets a broader context and engages in the challenges of feminist theory and therapy to traditional mental health. Chapters Four and Five set forth a model of feminist therapy which participates in its further development.

CHAPTER THREE

INTEGRATION AND CONTENT

THE first chapter of this book presented a selective essay on the history of feminism, spanning more than a century and touching at least four countries. It describes the diversity of thought, breadth of issues and a number of individuals instrumental in the development of feminism. The chapter introduces mental health workers to the broad historical/social content of feminism and to the variety of issues and emphases involved in a feminist viewpoint of women's nature and status. Such prospects are not ordinarily considered by practitioners and theorists in the mental health disciplines.

The century of vision and energy selectively presented in the first chapter stands in sharp contrast to the second chapter's subject. In reviewing the literature and describing the current status, the second chapter focuses narrowly on the decade of development of feminist therapy in the United States. Once again, both the focus upon women and the diversity of emphases are reinforced. The issues involved in women's nature and status defined in feminisms' historical development are still contemporary concerns within feminist therapy. The circumstances of some of the issues may have changed, as for example in birth control, although reproductive rights and control of their own bodies remain a focal concern today, as they were with Margaret Sanger. Economic factors and post-industrial woes have combined with the advocacy for fair employment practices in today's employment conditions for women, bringing some changes to women's employment data. Yet equal rights in employment is a central issue of present day feminists as it was for their sisters. Many women today continue to be unable to support themselves; economic autonomy remains an unrealized goal for many women in oppressive economies today as it has been for the last century. Role and marriage structures, sexuality, childcare, career options, education, male controlled conceptualizations of women's nature, political and social involvement, psychological and economic autonomy continue today to be fundamental issues in women's status. The historical and transnational perspective lent in the first chapter forces the understanding that feminist therapy responds to widespread, longterm, systematic issues for women and to feminist analysis of oppression.

The diversity of emphases within feminism presented in Chapter One is seen again in Chapter Two. The diversity illustrates the pluralism of feminism. It embraces the existence of many views of the questions surrounding women's status and potential, yet the diversity is unified by fundamental principles of feminism. The underlying principles are the common threads which tie present to the past and join the different emphases within feminism together in defining its focus and theory. The unifying feminist views are briefly stated here. The principles are discussed more fully later in the chapter. There is an acknowledgment and an analysis of women's oppression and a commitment to change women's oppression. There is the need to organize data and develop a mode of analysis which transcends the repression of information and the limiting structure of thought thus escaping the control of knowledge. Unified in these characteristics, the diverse emphases within feminism may be characterized in general terms as liberal or reformist, socialist or politico, and radical (Freeman, 1974; Jaggar, 1977).

The liberal or reformist feminist position is that women do not have equal status with men. This position lacks a historical or causative analysis, claiming only that the unequal status between the sexes is problematic for women in a variety of economic, social, interpersonal and psychological ways. It limits their full development and their options; it punishes certain behavior (i.e. assertiveness, instrumental action); it limits access to positions of status, influence and socially valued power. The liberal feminists' commitment to change these limitations is focused around equal rights for women. Liberal feminists concentrate their efforts on a variety of areas which they see as facilitating this change such as the documentation of inequality in education, work career options, sex roles, power positions within industry, government, religion, politics and the family. They attempt to raise awareness and change customs, attitudes, policy and laws which influence, reinforce and determine unequal status. This includes work around the Equal Rights Amendment, day care, reproductive rights, affirmative action, Title IX legislation, sex role awareness workshops, math phobia groups, sex-fair vocational and educational counseling. They promote safe houses for abused women, the creation of support and mentor networks with industry, education, government and the development of women's organizations or caucuses in the professions. Another level of activity of liberal feminists is research writing, consulting and advocating for change within the traditional institutions and professions. This work relies upon uncovering treatment based on myth or sexist attitudes and developing data to confirm nonstereotyped abilities while investigating differences between the sexes and carefully assessing the implications. They create educational programs to change sexist attitudes and demand nonsexist policies and procedures. Liberal or reformist feminists work toward a goal of equality in social/economic structures and cultural/personal options where both men and women will choose among equal and open options in creating their lifestyles and work. They wish to reform the present social/economic conditions so equal treatment is accorded both men and women.

Socialist or "politico" feminists may be involved in any of the activities of the reformist feminists; bettering women's conditions is also a clear priority for them. However, they do analyze the causes of women's oppression and link women with other oppressed groups. Socialist, Marxist and anarchist feminists, the variations within this grouping, may place the emphasis on different factors. All see the division of labor according to sex, the existing economic system and political process (Capitalism with the concommitant competition, control and self interest; hierarchical forms, and valuing of wealth and power) as the fundamental causes of oppression.

These feminists are committed to changing the Capitalistic economic system and creating other economic and political structures and forms of human interaction. These created structures would have very different processes and rewards, cooperation and concern for equity would oppose selective hierarchy and individual power and status.

Socialist feminists regard women's oppression as complex, many faceted, and continuing until basic social systems are changed. These feminists, therefore, work to change economic and political structures as well as human interaction. They have developed collaborative living environments, collective economic structures, egalitarian human relationships and interactive processes which are nonhierarchical and truthfully democratic. For example, shared or rotating leadership, consensus decision making, worker owned businesses, self-help services, egalitarian professional and organizational relationships are among their explorations and achievements. Their goals are clear, but there is no blueprint for what ought to be. The need for transformation and reorganization of basic social/economic structures remains very clear. Values, political and economic structures and human interactions must support equal and affirmative participation for all. This must be accomplished through an honoring of equally valid differences in belief, culture, language-pluralism.

The radical feminists are a very diverse group. They are unified in the position that patriarchy (male domination and control) is the causative factor for women's oppression. They hold that every aspect of current society has been shaped or influenced through male domination. This includes not only the economic and political systems and their allied supports of education, the professions, law and religion, but also the very content and shape of knowledge, history and its organization of data. They also believe that social forms (i.e., heterosexual couples, nuclear families, and the mores, values, and forms of discourse of our culture as well as content deemed valid or important, and the legitimacy awarded achievements) are all results of male dominance and women's oppression.

Radical feminists' visions for change are many, but often include the need to reject the current results of male dominance and to create new women-centered structures, forms, content and processes. Analysis and speculation occur in many areas, from discussions regarding women's nature, to woman-centered history, religion, and value systems, to creations in the arts, symbols and relationships, to political/social/economic organizations which evolve from women's values, process and consciousness and lead to women's relationships, sexuality and spirituality. Radical feminists are attempting to bring about human relationships, alternative cultures and political/economic organizations which evolve from women's expertise and visions. The rediscovery and creation of a woman-based culture is a radical feminist commitment. Their methods are often as diverse as their interests, ranging from dialogue through overt conflict with traditional forms, to the development of alternatives, entirely separate from traditional societal structures and processes.

Radical feminists are involved in developing women's centers and education or service environments and processes, in establishing alternative living structures and relationships, creating modes of worship, encouraging woman owned and run businesses, and in women-oriented professional services. They work on formal intellectual levels to develop women's knowledge of their history, and to create new ways of thinking and theoretical constructs and research methods as well as new modes of interacting with the environment. The woman poet living in a lesbian collective, the mental health professional daring to be a friend to a client and an advocate for women rather than for the state or profession, the physician who teaches women healing and health skills, the academic positing a new metaphysics, all are committed to the process of exploring and creating ways to end women's oppression and transform the nature, quality, content, and process of women's lives.

Feminists, both therapists and nontherapists, have confronted the mental health profession with evidence of its biases and deficiencies in its treatment of women. Workers in the field of mental health must have an understanding of both the history and present complexity of the feminist movement if they are to address these issues in any depth with hope for meaningful change. Feminists are saying, in effect, that there is an essential body of knowledge which mental practitioners presently ignore in the treatment of women who are emotionally distressed, knowledge which profoundly challenges present therapeutic practices and mental health institutions. In order to not do women harm, and to make health institutions more effective in helping women deal with their problems, program planners, administrators and therapists need to be able to demonstrate an awareness and respect for this knowledge.

Generally, however, the mental health field has been slow to become involved with women's issues, accepting for nearly a century the implicit assumption that females should be judged and treated on male criteria. Lower standards and sex role stereotyped expectations were used since they were considered to be less than males (Broverman, 1970; Hare-Mustin, 1983). The principles and sociopolitical analyses of feminism are not often considered by practitioners and theorists in the mental health disciplines. However, with the attention of the 1960s and 1970s to women in mental health, through the women's movement generally and the psychology of women specifically, mental health professionals have become somewhat more attentive to women's issues.

Since Chesler's book attacking the sexist assumptions and harmful practices of mental health practitioners' double standard of mental health, and Weisstein's critique of sexism in the theory and research methods of academic psychology, continuous work within mental health professions has occurred. There have been tremendous numbers of articles, studies, books and conferences carrying the confrontation with traditional mental health theory and practice further, generating new knowledge and practices which do not participate in sexism. For example, in 1980, Worell surveyed over 500 articles on the topic of counselling women alone. Aside from the publication of articles in the usual professional journals, there are currently three journals which publish solely within the area of the psychology of women, *Sex Roles, Psychology of Women Quarterly,* and *Women and Therapy.* Feminist women working within professional structures have developed ethical principles for practice with women, quidelines for nonsexist research and syllabi and references for course development. Challenges and development of services continue from outside of the professions.

The development of psychology of women as an area of research/study provided a bridge for these challenges and therapeutic strategies from within and outside the professions to the mental health establishment.

The psychology of women serves as a prototype of the change of a traditional discipline through feminist thought. Voices outside the professions demand, some within the profession hear and begin the work in professionally appropriate modes (articles, research, critique, model building) of transforming the disciplines and professions. Thus the psychology of women presents a broader context for understanding the sub-area of feminist therapy.

It should be understood that psychology is used here in a generic sense, as the study of human behavior and not in the parochial sense as the academic departments or profession. Here the topic — psychology — spawns many narrowly conceived and defined academic areas and professions: social work (Moskol), psychiatry (Seiden, Baker-Miller), counseling (Herman, Greenspan), clinical (Brodsky, Rawlings). Psychology then, as used in the psychology of women, represents a topic, that of women demanding attention and influence in all the human behavior and mental health disciplines and professions.

The psychology of women is a developing area within the mental health disciplines. The identifiable influences and contributions include, along with many others: the women's movement, grass roots women involved with mental health, human potential and Eastern influences, feminist scholars critical of traditional mental health theory, such as Mitchel and Chodorow, women within the disciplines and professions like Chesler, Weisstein, Tennov, Broverman, Seiden, Carter, and Rawlings, and current researchers like Wallston, Carlson, and Gilligan. Amid this diversity, there is a unifying force: a commitment to investigate, challenge and correct sexism in mental health at all levels. The work of the psychology of women continues in many different, but related areas: the development of paradigmatic and research methods, the analysis and critique of traditional practices and theory, and the generation of alternative theory and therapeutic procedures. This work challenges the present attitudes, theories and functions of mental health staffs and organizations, the policies of mental health professions and their methods of training practitioners.

The psychology of women is not merely generating new information about women that has been overlooked in previous theory, research, and practice; it is challenging the field of mental health at all its levels, academic, practice, policy, personnel and structure; it is calling for radical transformation.

Examples of this challenge to transformation abound, from Chesler's, Weisstein's, and Broverman's early documentation of sexism and the neglect of and damage to women at the various levels of the mental health professions through the scholarly analysis and critique of theory and research as in Carlson and Unger, to the creation of women based theory and research, exemplified by Baker-Miller and Gilligan. Feminist therapy both informs and is informed by this challenge to transformation that the psychology of women offers to the traditional theory and practice of the mental health profession.

Feminist philosophy and therapeutic practice is given a voice within the psychology of women, a voice speaking the language of the mental health establishment that can be heard by mental health practitioners. While the impact of the psychology of women upon the study of psychology may be ignored or trivialized by many, its effects are undeniable.

This impact can be traced and documented through an examination of the literature on the psychology of women. This literature is extensive, comprised of contributions by feminists from many fields within the various mental health professions and academic disciplines, as well as from other fields within the academy, and still others outside both the academy and the mental health professions.

The literature contains narrative accounts of women's experiences in therapy and the mental health system as well as analyses of women's status as relates to mental health. Both document such problems as the majority of therapists being male while the majority of clients are women (Grove, 1980), that discriminatory treatment of women is prevalent and outright abuse of women clients is tolerated in mental health services (Brodsky, 1975; Smith and David, 1975). In addition, there is literature which critiques the traditional and puts forth new conceptualizations of theory, pathology, health, development and healing. The impact of the psychology of women, through this literature, can be seen in many areas. Practices in publishing: journals no longer accept articles with sexist language; research: division 35 of APA nonsexist research guidelines; therapy: division 17 of APA nonsexist ethical guidelines; and professional organization: through women's caucuses and divisions forcing awareness of women, all reflect the impact of the psychology of women in the uncovering of and change in sexist practices.

The impact of women's psychology upon psychology can also be seen in the appearance or newly reconceptualized reappearance of many topics of significance to women. Clinical syndromes, sex roles, socialization, rape, domestic violence, male/female interactions, androgyny, sexism in assessment and diagnosis are impacting upon the traditional subareas within psychology. For example, questions relating to socialization, sex roles, sexist attitudes, discrimination and lifestyle choices are now being addressed in both development and social psychology. Cognitive psychology (learning and perception) reflects the impact by engaging questions and models of learned helplessness, social learning theory, bias in perceiving and organizing data and in personal schemas.

The psychology of women is changing traditional areas within psychology by including new topics, positing, developing, or adapting models, expanding factors in interactions and emphasizing new perspectives to old questions. The claim is not that these challenging questions have become central in the traditional areas. Rather, each of the traditional areas now includes among their members, and in their published literature, researchers and research focusing upon these questions, central to women's psychology and women's experience.

The impact of the psychology of women is also visible in the development of new courses and clinical specialities addressing women's experience, and the existence of these courses and specialities within the curricula of academic departments and mental health services. Courses such as the Psychology of Women, Sex Roles, Counseling Women, and Practice in Women's Services, exist in significant number in various mental health academic departments in universities and professional schools. Similarly, clinical specialties in women's services, therapy and groups have become identifiable in mental health practice. Professional associations also have committees, caucuses, and divisions directed toward women's issues and concerns. The impact of the psychology of women upon the traditional subareas of the study and practice of psychology, can be seen through changes in the curricula, the clinical specialties, and the professional associations.

Feminism as a philosophical stance and a political ideology (discussed more fully in the next section) requires more than an inclusion of a gender and relevant topics. It raises fundamental questions not only about the content of the discipline, but also about the nature, values, standards of knowledge, the methods of research, the legitimization and dissemination of information, the purposes and power structure of the discipline/profession. Some of these fundamental feminist challenges are beyond the scope of this book, and some are discussed in the following chapters. There are, however, several which fall within the context of the impact of the psychology of women upon traditional psychology.

Direct challenges to the philosophy of science, questioning the metaphysical and epistemological assumptive basis of the discipline, would probably require a radical feminist with a classical education in philosophy. Few of those exist within the discipline/profession of psychology. However, there are a number of feminist psychologists who are raising questions about the implications and restrictiveness of the research methodology within traditional psychology. So if not directly, then indirectly, traditional assumptions within psychology regarding reality and knowing are being critically analyzed. Weisstein, Carlson, and to some extent Wallston are questioning the value free claims, linear models, reductionism, and internal processes of the empirical models used within traditional psychological research methodology. Their voices are joined by many others who are calling for or actually using other research methodologies. Phenomenologically based methodologies are beginning to appear, whether they are simple self-report for C-R group research, the more complex designs used by Gilligan, or the development of sophisticated content analysis by Gottschalk. The feminist challenge of women's psychology to traditional psychology is to be more inclusive and accepting of alternative methodologies while at the same time recognizing the limits and deficiencies of the use of empirically based methodologies.

Johnson, Grady, and O'Leary point out the underlying sexist assumptions often seen in the conceptualization and asking of research questions, hypothesis formulation, variable selection, measurement and selection of subjects and control groups. Feminists are questioning the political reality reflected in the acceptance and publication rate of manuscripts that address new topics of analysis, or that question research methods themselves. Wallston, Kaplan, and Sedney are discussing the human and political implications of the use of empirical data, which is identified as limited and often biased, in the creation of social policy. They are requiring experience, relevance, and political awareness as the explicit guides for selection of areas and hypothesis development in psychological research.

Another impact of the psychology of women on traditional psychology is an emphasis upon an interdisciplinary approach to both theory and practice. Women's psychology finds its guide to topic selection in women's actual experience. The goals of women's psychology are analysis of the phenomena and exploration of change. Its commitment is to the fullest possible understanding and the most effective change. Therefore, arbitrary and possessively guarded disciplinary boundaries are seen to be irrelevant. Interdisciplinary collaboration in approach and methods are used. For example, it is not unusual to find a feminist historian, sociologist and psychologist academics working together on the topic of rape. Each brings her own analytic bases, literature and research perspectives, and attempts to work together with the other two for a fuller understanding of rape than any could have achieved singularly. Collaboration in formerly distinct subareas with psychology is also occurring. The study of socialization, for instance, includes elements of social learning, perception, developmental and personality psychology. Cognitive restructuring includes clinical/counseling, personality and cognitive psychology. The study of sex roles requires social, personality, developmental, organizational, cognitive, and biophysiological areas within psychology, and has clearly benefitted from sociological, anthropological, historical, and biological perspectives and research. The effectiveness of the psychology of women's interdisciplinary approach, in its concerns and research, challenges the usefulness of traditional disciplinary barriers and professional territorialism.

The cross pollinization of conceptualization across subareas in psychology and other academic disciplines is present in the theory of women's psychology. In the early part of its decade of development, descriptive critique of traditional theories and models was emphasized. Some of these critiques were sophisticated, serious, substantial, and some were exercises in scathing rhetoric. These critiques uncovered obvious and embedded sexism, both through misogyny and through omission, within psychological theories and models.

They showed the need for the inclusion of women, for the admission of the uniqueness of women's conditions, and for the study of the oppression of women in psychological theory. After this investigative uncovering, and this serving of notice, feminist psychologists began to build models and to post theories based upon women's experience. Both functions continue within feminist theory in women's psychology. Chesler, Broverman, and Tennov provide examples of the critiques. Dinnerstein, Baker-Miller, and Gilligan provide samples of model and theory building.

The critique continues on sophisticated levels and is gaining more acceptance, or at least attention, in traditional spheres within the professions, as demonstrated by the recent analysis of women's treatment under the DSM III, published in the *American Psychologist* (1983), the major journal disseminated to all members by APA, the central professional association for psychologists. The theory building is exciting and sometimes controversial. It includes, for example, the study of biologically based sex differences, fear of success, sex roles ascription, learned helplessness, women's moral development and psychoanalytic bias against women.

Alternative services for women have a somewhat different history than research and theory. Until very recently, they have developed mainly outside traditional mental health systems. Their genesis has been in community women's centers and in the private or collective practices of feminist therapists. However, with more women mental health professionals working within the traditional system (by volition or forced to by the press from centralized and controlled funding sources), feminist oriented mental health services are beginning to function even within traditional mental health services. Feminist treatment, buttressed by women's psychology, has impacted services as seen in alcoholism treatment, YWCAs, community counseling centers, career services, and some residential programs. So while the women's psychological services and supports have developed and continue outside of traditional service systems, the demand for and creation of feminist oriented mental health services and supports for women has impacted upon even the traditional agencies of service provision.

The psychology of women is the bridge carrying feminism to the traditional mental health and the academic/professional home of feminist therapy. The impact of the psychology of women is diverse, multifaceted and continuing. However, there are identifiable principles in women's psychology. Four in particular unite each of the areas of impact already discussed and will orient future development.

First, research, theory and model building should be based upon the experience of women. This principle, simple in its stated form, has profound implications. The demand is for centrality of experience. This stands in sharp contrast to current methods of selection of topics, by potential for publication or funding sources, mentor defined or idiosyncratic whim. It also challenges the use of generaic human-male or power structure defined focus, for example management orientations in organizations research or teacher and curricular focus in education. This principle proclaims the validity of women's experience and demands its use as a criterion in analysis, theory and research. Experience and women's experience are inseparable from knowledge and its generation.

The second principle is the demand for intra- and interdisciplinary research, as discussed earlier in this chapter. The third is a commitment to changingthe oppression of women in its multitudinous forms. This principle embodies the political orientations of women's psychology. In the academy, the profession and offered services, political neutrality is claimed. However, this claim is false. The academy, research, theory, the professions, and traditional mental health services are indeed political. They maintain and reinforce the status quo, which is sexist. The politics of women's psychology is feminist, clearly articulated and committed to change.

The fourth principle is a critical stance toward assumptions, dogmas, and practices of traditional psychology, stemming from the belief that traditional psychology reflects the biases of the culture. This does not mean that all traditional theory, research and practices are discarded, but they must be closely inspected for oppression, sexism, and reinforcement of the status quo, as well as for arbitrary and limited methods and assumptions.

These principles not only direct and inform the development of the psychology of women, but they clarify its feminist orientation as well. This further demonstrates the psychology of women bridging function between feminism and traditional mental health, and illustrating the supportive structure and actual fabric which surrounds feminist therapy. Having forged the connections among traditional mental health disciplines/professions, feminism, the psychology of women, and feminist therapy, we now turn to the context for this book: a feminist view of mental health.

Women with belief, knowledge and experience in feminism, its analysis and its alternative culture, are colliding with traditional mental health on a number of levels. Some are clients seeking assistance with the resolution of conflict caused by their lived contradictions and the resulting psychological damage between their feminism and the demands of the dominant culture. Some women are advocates of feminism confronting traditional mental health. Some are researchers and theory builders while others are reformers of traditional practices and policy. Some women are outside of traditional mental health in private or collective practices or in women's centers providing services whose very existence stands as a critique to traditional mental health practices and policy. These women are the lifeblood, the spokespersons, the shapers of feminist therapy and a feminist orientation to mental health. Their needs, their analyses and their creations are the building blocks of a feminist orientation to therapy and mental health. There is neither agreement nor monolithic belief among them but all are guided by the shaped principles and informed by the diversity in feminism. When then is the feminist framework?

Recognizing diversity while building a view which involves shared positions, the following section presents a feminist framework of mental health. The framework draws from and integrates the first two chapters as well as the many aspects, the psychology of women, feminism, the multilevel concerns, the critique of traditional mental health, calling for change in practices and transformation in beliefs and structure, and the principles and assumptions of feminist therapy; all interweave, flowing into and out of this feminist framework. In the following discussion of the feminist framework, feminist views of women, of mental health, and of therapy are each in turn considered.

One of the key pieces in a feminist view of women, is reliance on women's experience. Women's experience as felt, lived and processed is the trusted base for knowledge. Potential bias is acknowledged, and serious attempts are made, to clarify and articulate the experience. This consciousness raising process seeks its validation through generalization among many women's experience, rather than in fitting with traditionally accepted theories and organization of knowledge. Information coming from standard theories and causative explanations are systematically inspected for sexism in motivation, assumption, method and goal.

Another closely related key aspect of a feminist view of women is a recognition of the tremendous diversity in women's experience. Just as psychologists believe such factors as cognitive structures, motivation, developmental and present events, and family norms shape one's personality and perception, so too feminists believe that class, race, ethnicity, culture, sexual identification, and lifestyle shape one's experience. Some feminists hold that these latter factors are powerful determiners of one's experience and that these cause existence to be different among people. The acknowledgement of differing realities for women is an ever shaping focus for feminists.

Decreasing one's own ethnocentrism and increasing one's awareness or diversity through self education is seen as a responsibility by feminists. This self education may be accomplished through reading lectures, cultural experiences, talking with women of different classes, races, cultures, and so on. Analysis of one's own biases and reflection on others' experiences are important in the process. Many feminists make strong commitments to facilitate increased appreciation of women's differences.

Another key piece of a feminist view is the acknowledgement of the relationships among all who have not shaped the dominant values in U.S. mental health theory and practice: non-white races, non-western cultures, non-adult populations, non-male people, non-dominant religions and ideologies, and non-privileged classes. At non-superficial levels, a feminist view holds that entire reconceptualizations and transformations are needs because what is assumed, valued, believed, normed for behavior, determined as goals and established as criteria, has been shaped by a relatively few white adult males. Dynamics of oppression have some similarities among varying groups. The factors of non-dominance vary as does the presentation of oppression. But the powerlessness and the distance from the unattainable pinnacle of the hierarchy forge a relationship among all oppressed groups.

Feminists hold that all women are oppressed by sexism. They may differ in additional oppression through racism, classism, culturalism and ageism. Sexist oppression and the misogynist attitudes which support and stem from it, are responsible for many of the problems women face. Women's internalization of the devaluation and powerlessness of sexism complete the damage. Externally, women are presented and treated as less than men and they come to believe this. The result is double edged, external discrimination and internal self doubt.

Commitment to social change, developing structures and processes which value women and the discovery/creation of women's unoppressed nature are quintessential foundations in a feminist view.

Efforts to effect social change on many levels ranging from uncontaminating the sexist data about women to transforming power relations and functional values in political and economic and social structures is seen as necessary and desirable. Equally important is the development of structures and processes which value women and allow full and equal participation. Interpersonal interactions and social forms stemming from cooperation, openness, enabling growth, equal access to power and resources, valid knowledge, and pluralistic development are guiding principles in the struggle to develop these new forms. It should be noted that this struggle involves many debates and differences, even among committed feminists.

While there are certainly other substantial voices critical of the status quo, feminism has a deep and varied analysis, one which demands not only social, political and interpersonal change but paradigmatic and value transformations. A feminist view also has structures for change and an understanding of both the complexity and interrelationship. Yet feminism is not monolithic and set, it is still evolving and is often quite humble about solutions or the correct answers. Indeed, feminism may better be seen reorienting and creating vision rather than as an articulation of the will to impose particular ends. A feminist view calls for multilevel reconceptualization and transformation but it does so with a different kind of analysis: one that is evolving, developing, not final. Different realities are being seen, discovered and created but they must be developed and made real. The feminist analysis is a reorienting vision, a process of agentry, responsibility and health, allowing women the responsibility for their lives, and giving the skills necessary to negotiate the environment.

A feminist position related to mental health flows from a feminist view of women. It requires profound change in the conceptualization and structure of traditional mental health. The analysis and change demands of feminism call for significant changes in traditional mental health. The reconceptualization of economic, political, and social structures and processes would create substantially different views of mental health, interpersonal interactions, and personal development for women and men. Social conditions, power relations, interactive processes, values, and world views all would be radically altered. Knowledge, theory, the professions, access and legitimacy would all be quite different. In mental health, feminism does not have one firm alternative theoretical body, nor does it have one answer for the shape of the change. Rather it is critiquing (identifying sexism, pointing out bias), inviting theorizing, and developing different values, criteria, functions, organizations, structures, processes and relations. The best it can do is analyze, point out flaws and guide in the creation of new systems of thought content areas, professional organizations and notions of helping.

In mental health, feminism's pluralism extends to oppressed groups, non-dominant cultures and values, as well as ways of knowing. Criterion for mental health, underlying assumptive bases of health and right living, goals of treatment, legitimized ways of knowing beyond expert and rational/empirical, are all challenged to expand through feminism. As one of the many examples, feminism calls for egalitarian, not hierarchical, relationships, interactions and social systems.

The functional concepts of egalitarianism are power of definition and right to bargain. If these concepts of egalitarianism were applied to mental health, radical changes would be wrought. No longer would the American Psychiatric Association enjoy its arbitrary power to define what is pathological, and many potential helpers, including nonprofessionals, might join the negotiation process for reimbursement. Licensing and certification boards would demand demonstration of competence instead of the current apprenticeship requirements. Research would be awarded merit on the basis of its usefulness and broad base contribution to pluralistic notions of realities rather than as it is now, on its power to control, and conceptual reducationism. Clients and therapists would join together in naming and prioritizing the definition of difficulties and the direction for change efforts instead of the social standard reinforcement by elite power groups now used. These changes do recognize that all are not equal in skill, understanding, experience, or analysis. They also recognize the need for assistance in adapting to these changes. As one example, mental health workers have all been trained in structures and mechanisms opposed to egalitarian relationships. The power of definition, right to bargain, valuing diversity and nonattribution of power arbitrarily, are not taught to mental health workers. In fact, expert professional judgement is expected. Learning to catch one when self imposing power, defining and withholding negotiation rights, is a large task, one requiring individual and structural change. It will require vigilance of both one's own functioning and the functions of institutions.

Feminism is participating with other voices in breaking down the compartmentalization of knowledge. In mental health it is no longer adequate to be limited to only intrapsychic forces in the personality. Social forces, family dynamics, class, sex, race, institutionalized patterns, and so on, all shape personality. No longer is it acceptable to proclaim narrowly the boundaries of the personal and to leave other influencing factors to sociology, organizational development, anthropology, history and political science. Feminism demands broad conceptualization, based on the experience, not on the artificial boundaries of traditional disciplines. Mental health is multi-shaped and the many influencing factors must be attended to. In the process, decompartmentalization of information, and perspective through the intermix of formerly discipline bounded corpi of knowledge, will occur.

Feminism in mental health also means starting with women's experience and using this experience to identify the specific difficulties and criterion for model building, theory creation and research investigation. Specific life and developmental issues for females (i.e., violence against women, psychological concommitents of fusion, the psychic effects of social powerlessness, mothering, pathological potential of sex role ascription) become topics and content areas of relevance. Models built upon women's experience have been developed, as for example, Horner's fear of success, or Janeway's powers of the weak. Theory also has been developed which is based solidly upon and relating directly to women's experience, as seen in Gilligan's women's moral development and Dinnerstein's reoriented expansion of objection relationships.

As already discussed, a substantial change would also occur in research methodologies when women's experience became central. As women's experience, instead of traditional male defined theory and restrictive research processes, continues to inform mental health, and as mental health feminists continue to expand their conceptualizations, mental health theory and research, content of relevance, and practice habits will continue to change dramatically.

The feminist view of therapy is consistent with both a feminist view of women and mental health. Together, the three comprise the feminist framework. Therapy, its practice, habits, and interventions are being significantly reoriented through feminism. Feminism participates in the uncovering of the pervasive power of dominant, male oriented middle class, capitalistic values in society's functioning. Feminism articulates this impact on social structure, individuals and psychic function for women. During this process, traditional mental health theory and criteria for pathology are seen to be preserving the status quo, useful only to one privileged segment of the population. Conceptualization of health, goals of therapy, and procedures in practice all must be challenged.

Middle class educated white males, supportive of the social/economic status quo, are the group benefitted by traditional conceptualizations of therapy. Extant are theories which posit authoritative analysis of executive structures controlling warring innate drives and moral sanctions (psychodynamic). There are expert behavioral engineers manipulating reinforcements to control the behavior of individuals who are viewed as blank slates awaiting proper programming (behaviorism). Also exists the proselytizing of individual freedom and potential by entrepreneurs with capital and slick gurus (human potential movement). These are models and modes compatible with the dominant social views but not with the realities of human nature and real experience.

These therapy and theory conceptualizations do not speak, for example, to the reality of the black ghetto women whose sense of worth and needs for survival come from the very things and actions which bar her from white male middle class success. Nor do they speak to the single mother who uses her Aid to Dependent Children funds to live in a collaborative house which also functions as a safe refuge for battered women. Nor do they speak to the divorced middle class working mother, made to worry about her son's lack of competitiveness, except to blame her for bad mothering and not providing a male role model. Traditional conceptualizations are discordant with pluralistic women's realities and experience. Feminist therapy not only names their inappropriateness and damage, but is developing very different conceptualizations and practices.

Feminist therapy challenges the dichotomous conceptualizations such as strong/weak, male/female, intellect/emotion, pathology/health that are inherent in conventional therapy. It also challenges power relations such as professional/patient, expert/ignorant, manager/worker, inherent in conventional practice. Instead, feminist therapy articulates the harmful impact and the damage done through these conventional conceptualizations and practices, and seeks to change both the social structures and therapy which reinforce them. One example of this change is seen in feminist therapies' conceptualization of self which is in sharp contrast to traditional therapies' notions.

Feminist therapies' views of self include a strong social dimension of being, both in the sense of being shaped by social forces and in the sense of being responsible to others. This view also includes the process of continual development and the possibility of selecting among limited choices, whose consequences must be analyzed. This view of self also contends that one must self define and select values and award oneself the personal attribution of power. It also acknowledges the contradictions and dangers women experience in being powerless in male defined terms, while possessing very real strength and spirit independent of the roles ascribed in social power systems. Just as feminism is breaking down the bounded disciplines for interdisciplinary perspectives, so too is feminist therapy breaking down the distinct and narrow theories with their compartmentalization of self, replacing them with views of an integrated whole which is multi-infuenced and multifaceted. Complexity, interaction, and damage from hostile environments are central in the conception of self in feminist therapy.

Feminist social analysis and view of self are integral to feminist therapy and they guide its practice. There are several features which illustrate the relationship quite clearly.

Feminist therapy understands that being a woman is a process. Change and reconceptualization are central parts of that process. Over time and within each individual, different areas need attention and focus. Development of social conditions and individual awareness, which allow change toward the feminist view of self, is a long and complex committment. Feminist therapy is also based in pluralism. There is no single, final, or right criterion for mental health, right living, valuing or action for individuals espoused in feminist therapy. There are many useful change strategies, and choices are different and shifting. Health is seen as engaging in the process of analysis, development, creation and choice for self and in relation to other people and social forces.

Therapy cannot be separated from women's lives. The relationship of oppressive conditions, self hate, misogynist conceptualization, needs to transform one's own cognitions and self attributions, and social forces are unified. Further, therapeutic activities must focus upon the individual but also on unhealthy social conditions. The process of therapy mirrors or is mirrored by social actions, increased women's consciousness and supportive community development. Therapy becomes united with living, and that process continues to develop feminism on both practical and theoretical levels. In turn, this informs and challenges psychological theory and practice. Feminist therapy is eclectic with a feminist perspective. The issue is not which theory or change strategy is right. Therapy/living is far more complex than any one psychological theory. Also, psychological theories to date compartmentalize human nature, continue a discipline bounded perspective, and are linear. None of these are in keeping with women's reality. The oppositional, manipulative, strictly interpsychic or genetic or environmental, simple choice assumptions of traditional psychological theory are wrong, naive, and harmful. Feminist therapy holds that external social, economic, political, cultural, class, race, and interpersonal conditions felt in

women's lives through sex discrimination, sex role behavior and attitudes, and internalized in family, relationships, and self image, are
the causes of pathology. Some pathology is too severe for direct use
of feminist therapy; some women are too damaged. However, many
women develop agentry (a goal of feminist therapy). So feminist
therapy does not impose any model of health but rather seeks to assist women in evolving and developing their own critique, analysis,
skills, options, and criteria. It also helps women transform devaluation of self, other women, and external male defined criteria, to valuing self and other women, further gaining skills and supporting
women, as well as evolving and developing their own criteria.
Neither blaming nor glorifying the victim (made victim through social and personal oppression, and self hating through sexism),
feminist therapy seeks to re-educate, increase options, develop skills,
reconceptualize, build supportive communities, and challenge
women to make their own choices.

Feminist therapy does not impose value positions, life choices or
criteria on women. Positions on self/other, internal/external,
individual/social, self/collective are not proscribed. Indeed, conceptualizing these dichotomous ways is at odds with the view. However,
feminist therapy does aim to facilitate awareness of the interactions
and acknowledges different chosen styles and differing needs. Informed choice with knowledge of consequences, based on unique
needs and particular points of development, is the goal.

Feminism brings a different view of the role of the therapist to
therapy. Demands for egalitarian interaction is one basis for the
transformation. Egalitarian relationships, discussed in Chapter
Two, do not assume a false equalness. Obviously there are differences between therapist and client, in knowledge, perspective,
damage, development, and choices. And the therapist is committed
to assisting the client. Basically egalitarian demands, that the power
of definition and the right to bargain, will be brought into the therapeutic interaction for all involved. It is these feminist views of equal
power in relationships which informs the Chapter Two discussion of
the nature of the therapeutic relationship in feminist therapy.

In keeping with feminist ideas on community and the need for
women to support one another, forms of therapy other than one-to-
one are a significant part of feminist therapy. Feminist therapy is

committed to groups, self help, reading, social action and women's community activities as part of the therapy because they are structures which may allow learning, change, support, exposure to alternative choice options, increased awareness, and broader consciousness. Within the context of client readiness and appropriateness, involvement in these activities are seen as useful and important for clients. Also, the feminist view as applied to the role of the therapist encourages continuing learning for the therapist. Increases in self knowledge about one's own needs, biases, limits, hierarchical assumptions, racism, classism, individualism, rhetorical demogoguery, are all necessarily an ongoing process. Community action, traditional mental health theory and practice critique, study groups, collaborations, and supervision are important continuing involvement for feminist therapists.

Feminism as a mode of analysis is not merely an intellectual form for academic discussion. Instead it is a vital developing reality which directly impacts upon conceptualizations and actions, on mental health and therapy.

The themes within the feminist framework will be discussed more thoroughly throughout the following chapters as we present a model of feminist therapy and indicate the content and structural as well as process changes necessary in traditional mental health training and service. Discussions are still lively in feminist therapy and the psychology of women. We present our model as a next step in the process of development. It is meant to stimulate discussion.

CONTEXT FOR THE BOOK

Feminist analysis of mental health and feminist therapy must be concerned with how the political becomes personal; the politics of emotions and choice; how women are affected by and internalize the social messages, attitudes and conditions of oppression; and how this process can be changed.

Feminism is not the first to critique the mental health system and therapy. But it provides a well grounded, comprehensive process of analysis. Nor are the ideas presented for changing traditional mental health unique only to feminist therapy, but they are systematic and compelling. The explication of the sexism in mental health and therapy has been ably achieved. The next step of working toward change of that sexism in its many levels and forms, is the task at hand.

Through feminism, both an analytical position and a commitment, we are calling for needed changes in the mental health system and presenting the development of feminist therapy. We are recommending a variety of changes which must occur if traditional mental health is to root out its embedded sexism and join in the process of developing the knowledge and practices that can contribute to the health of women. Guided by feminist aims of ending women's oppression, understanding systematic external causation, transforming power relationships, uncovering sexism, and creating pluralistic equality, our work calls for fundamental reconceptualization and change of the biased knowledge, practice, and assumptions in mental health. Our work challenges the too comfortably held perceptual sets and cognitive structures which reinforce traditional assumptions about mental health, and a politically free theory and practice. We name the power, the sexism and the oppression of women in which mental health colludes. Our sights are set on participating in the development of an approach to mental health which creates positive health and wellness, fully acknowledges the damage to women resulting from the environment in which they live and resulting from the experts who, blaming women, manipulate them into adjustment to hostile life conditions and controlled interpretations. We urge mental health workers to challenge the traditions, power structures, theory, training and practice which maintain the status quo and oppress women. Mental health professionals can no longer hide from the politics of their position by ignoring economic and social conditions.

Feminism makes clear the secondary status of oppressed groups, sexism, male defined theory, limited methods of research and modes of knowing, and non-egalitarian and manipulative professional relations which serve to repress and control deviation from status quo norms within traditional mental health. Feminism demands change and points the way toward creating that change.

In the next two chapters, we offer a systematic model of feminist therapy. We do not intend to present the answers but we do participate in a process of which we are committed: A process of developing ways to understand and facilitate the mental health of women.

CHAPTER FOUR
HARMFUL ADAPTATION

THIS chapter and the next present our model for feminist therapy. This chapter focuses upon the process of Harmful Adaptation, which is the term we use to refer to the self-negating, self-destructive learning outcome in the social cultural context for women. In this chapter, we also set forth assumptions on which our model rests, and we define some terms.

The next chapter deals with the two components that are necessary if feminist therapy is to become a system offering preventative as well as therapeutic services. The process of taking corrective action undoes the damage done to a woman during the harmful adaptation process. The process of health maintenance mobilizes feminist resources to change the environment of all women by working to eliminate sexism.

In many ways, our society is a hostile environment for women. Their learning and development, the conditions surrounding their existence and attitudes, as well as the actions toward women as a gender are not in accord with health. Full development of unique skills, opportunities to make informed and aware choices among real alternatives, and supportive structures encouraging analysis and action are not readily available for women within the dominant culture. Indeed, the commonly available evidence of women's poverty, secondary status, and lack of decision making access in professional, industrial, governmental, educational, and social policy is well documented. The statistics are grim. For example, 1983 World Health Organization statistics reveal that women do two-thirds of the world's work while receiving only one-tenth of the world's income.

69

Nationally, the final report of the National Advisory Council on Economic Opportunity (October 1981) shows that the vast majority of the poor are women and children; two out of every three poor adults are women, and families headed by women show a steady decline in economic status. Even a casual study of the current statistical abstracts prepared by the U.S. Department of Commerce, Bureau of the Census will further document the realities of women's status today.

As indicated in earlier chapters, varying feminist analyses posit the causes, supportive factors and enablers of the oppression of women in somewhat different directions. Socialist feminists hold economic and political systems responsible; radical feminists regard patriarchy as the source; liberal feminists examine employment patterns, laws and social attitudes in their attempt to dissipate sexism. Many contemporary feminists see the roots of women's oppression in the interaction of all these factors. Our purpose is to present the psychic link, not to engage in the analysis of root causes of sexism, discrimination, and devaluation of women. That is, we wish to discuss how these facts of discrimination, the oppressive structures which enable them, as well as sexist attitudes get translated into women's views of themselves and behaviors. Our concern is with the effects of sexism on women's self image, and their adjustment to interpersonal, social, and occupational interaction patterns. We also examine the culture's discriminatory attitudes as expressed in its beliefs about appropriate roles and options for women.

Sexism also affects the self image of men, their adjustment patterns and the views of society regarding their expected roles, alternatives and status. The oppressive structures of discrimination limit the options of many different groups of people. Our focus here, however, is on women. Without question, much that we propose and critique would apply to other oppressed, non-dominant groups as well as to the male gender. We hope that others will provide analyses and make appropriate applications; we shall not. It is our commitment to and our experience as women to which we address ourselves. It is not our intent to blame men in a simplistic analysis of the structures that support women's oppression. In a large part, men do dominate power systems and health service standards. However, they too are pieces, albeit more significant pieces in the larger puzzle. Men are constrained and delimited, too. Our model of feminist therapy is not anti-male but it is pro-female.

Although we hold that all women are harmed by the sexist bias of our social institutions, which devalues the contributions of women, we do not mean to imply that all women sustain severe psychological injury or that all women will require feminist therapy. Oppressive conditions exist for all women, but vary with the individual. Even in a repressive climate, we can see the positive results of the presence of a parent who rejects women's dependent role restrictions, a career mentor, or supportive friends. Further, the possession of extraordinary talent and the determination to use it may enable some women to move past traditional limitations and to minimize the damage of the environment to their self concepts. These women may develop strong and accurate images of themselves, as well as respect for their own and other women's abilities, making the therapeutic intervention of corrective action unnecessary for them. They can benefit, however, from participation in the health maintenance process, where their strengths can be celebrated, enhanced and shared with other women.

Power systems and health are two terms central to the discussion in these two chapters; both are complicated and used in rather abstract modes. We use the term *power systems* in the sense of organized groups and structures which have legitimized status that is culturally approved. Their influence and overt practices are directly or indirectly sanctioned by custom or law. They also provide dominant patterns for social and economic organization within society. Finally, their ideology and mode of operation becomes normative. They are societal standard setters and message bearers. Power systems have many functions, some of which may meet human needs, but reward is given only to those who conform.

Most people, except perhaps anarchists, would agree that consensual organization, influence and education are needed in society. The existence of power systems is not the issue. Rather it is the ideology, normative functions, operations and selective rewards which are the issues. Extant are hidden ideology, arbitrary and exclusionary normative standards, hierarchical and non-participative modes of functioning, which reward only those persons who conform. These are the dimensions which change the power systems in

America from necessary social organizers, educators, and influenc-
ers to dominators. Their domination of the social context sets standards, determines beliefs, and controls economic options and social
alternatives. The domination, control, and constraint functions of
power systems are often hidden, denied, or cloaked in exclusivity
and privilege. Further, the power systems in American society are
interlocking, functioning in the same hierarchical and non-
participative modes. They have similar ideologies; power is granted
to those strong enough to seize it. Control and manipulation are justified by self-serving goals. Success is based upon producing system-
serving results and conformity to arbitrary standards. Access to
policy determination and decision making, is exclusive and discriminatory. Power systems serve many functions and some of them
may be beneficial, but working separately and together, traditional
power systems present harmful models of behavior, devaluing attitudes and beliefs about the nature, status, and role of women.
Further, they manipulate and reward conformity to their standards
while they ignore or punish nonconformance.

Power systems, include familial, religious, educational, vocational, business, industrial, governmental, health and social service
provider structures. The alternatives these power systems offer for
women are limited and constraining. They cast women into dependent, self-negating positions in relation to other people and to the
power system itself. The images of women who are valued by power
systems and communicated as role models, are subordinate, self-
denying, givers of succor, nurturers of others, and doers of maintenance tasks. At best, present power systems place women at risk in
our society; at worst, they damage women. Power systems and their
effect on women's beliefs, behavior and self concepts will be discussed further in this chapter.

Mental health is the second central concept of our model of
feminist therapy. A feminist conception of mental health is particularly complex, since it must take into account the social constraints,
the damage done by a hostile, sexist environment: the psychological,
social and physical, and development of self as well as the nature of
women's interactions with others.

Conventional criteria for mental health, the dominant medical
model and behavior therapies, as well as reality therapy and its kind,

are not appropriate. The medical model holds mental health to be the absence of pathology. However, definition through absence is not useful. It does not indicate what a healthy relationship to other people, society, or the environment is, forcing acceptance of social norms and standards which cast women in dependent roles. Significant questions must be raised about the criteria used for pathology. The behavioral orientation of reality therapy and related theories use basic notions of effective behavior and responsible actions as criteria. However, they offer inadequate analysis of the determinants of effective behavior or responsible action, leaving one to again assume conformity to dominant social norms. Hence, adjustment to dominant social norms is the implicit or explicit notion of mental health within these orientations. Since dominant social norms are in large part determined by power systems, uncritical adjustment to them colludes with the power systems and has little to do with mental health.

Another set of notions, humanistic or third force, seek to set mental health within the individual. Generally these approaches (e.g., existential, Gestalt, self-theory) characterize mental health as engaging the processes of growth, individuality, and self determination. The mentally healthy person is seen as developing self-awareness, and being responsible for meeting her own needs, while also considering the needs of others. These approaches to mental health do have the benefit of placing mental health criteria within the individual and not with the adjustment and conformity to dominant social norms. For this reason, they have become very attractive to many people, particularly to those with a primary commitment to the person and specifically, in our context, to non-sexists and liberal feminists within the mental health service system. The problem with this orientation is that by placing the criteria for mental health in the individual, the analysis of the impact of social forces on women is neglected. For example, Rogers, a significant developer of self-theory, holds that human beings have an organismic need for development toward becoming fully functioning. Further, that in life or in therapy, this force will prevail if specific conditions such as unconditional positive regard, empathy, psychological contact, and genuineness, are met. The work of Rogers and others within this third force is important as it begins the process of characterizing positive mental health and sets criteria in the individual, not in social adjustment. However, the work lacks analysis of the role of social, political, and economic forces and their impact in shaping the self. Power systems manipulate images, beliefs, options, standards, and rewards for their own ends. These are often incompatible with positive individual development and growth toward full functioning, i.e., mental health. Those individuals most incongruent with the role model images of the power systems are damaged the most by being given the least. Oppressed groups and women who receive little reward and who are discriminated against in access and entry into the power systems are harmed. People who do not or cannot fit the images of the power systems: the old, disabled, differently cultured or colored, wrong sexed, these people cannot gain the social and economic rewards of money, status, and influence. They also cannot gain the psychological counterparts: a sense of worth, self acceptance, and motivation enabled by potential achievement. They are denied inclusion in the rewards and necessary conditions for growth. The third force's neglect of these dynamics is a tragic flaw, one which not only does not account for external forces in its conception, but which incorrectly places the total responsibility and obligation on the individual for her growth and development.

The conventional ideas about mental health are inappropriate for feminist therapy, but they may offer valuable pieces in building a conceptualization of mental health and a methodology for its achievement. The medical model does introduce attention to biophysical and internal process disruption. Behavior therapies engender consideration of the effects of learning. Reality therapy focuses attention on responsibility and actions. Self-theories contribute an emphasis on the process of self-development, appropriate conditions and conceptions of fully functioning, the quality of life and well-being, all concepts of positive mental health. Each of these conventional conceptions contributes valid considerations to the process of developing a feminist model of mental health. However, none is adequate to the task of defining or even characterizing mental health. Indeed, as they stand, each is counterproductive.

A conception of mental health appropriate for feminism has not yet been achieved. There are many people engaged in the process in a number of ways. Contributions include feminist utopian ideas, radical feminist notions of energy and connection with other women and the planet, feminist analysis of social and economic forces, feminist critique of conventional disciplines and knowledge bases, and feminist development and application of theory in mental health and modes of therapy. Certainly, progress has been made as the prime importance of women's experience, external forces, social constraints and their psychic link, and the need for holistic views are some of the parameters which have been clarified. We will use a set of constructs for mental health which share the clarified parameters and also participate in the process of developing a feminist theory of mental health.

The set of constructs used in this work relate both to central discussions of the developing feminist theories of mental health, and to the assumptions of our model of feminist therapy. These constructs are placed in the social context. They acknowledge that women are oppressed and that the images of women's nature and the roles imposed by various power systems as well as the status of women determined by the power systems are destructive to their mental health. Oppression disrupts development by curtailing options and tainting morality and psychology. It leads to: 1) the internalization of the power system images, values and standards — identification with the aggressor; or 2) a view which negates agentry, the ability and responsibility to act independently of external forces — a victim psychology — hopeless confusion, resigned helplessness and powerlessness leading to denial or withdrawal; or 3) anger and rebellion which in its best form leads to analysis and commitment to change.

Our constructs of mental health also accept the assumption of interdependence. At a conceptual level, interdependence requires holistic and systematic organization of reality. That is, that the whole is greater than the sum of its parts, that the whole is not reducible to its parts, and further that there are interactive relationships among the parts. Applying interdependence to women's experience leads to commitments to sisterhood, interaction between the internal and external, self in relation to others, human actions and planetary impacts of feminist ideals, interrelating of mind and body, connections between all people and people in their context: social systems, environment, history and identity. This assumption also implies that dichotomies such as agent versus victim be reconceptualized to the juncture of individual responsibility and social constraint, and that unitary stands on biological determinism, social determinism, or free will, be reconceptualized until each is interrelated and has an existence and impact which influences and modifies the others. This assumption is based on the fact that none can be reduced to a single causative or controlling factor.

Our constructs of mental health resting on the preceding assumptions are as follows: A healthy woman *experiences* herself as a woman. A strong aspect of her identity is being a woman. This identity includes both historical and contemporary links with other women. The experience of being a woman includes both devaluation and value as well as some sense of constraint and individual responsibility. A healthy woman is capable of *receiving* data from herself, others, and from the environment. She has not closed down or distorted her perceptual process. She remains open to the information from her own body, senses, and thoughts, from others' opinions, beliefs, experiences and analyses. She also remains open to information from the environment, including power systems' messages and actions, subcultural experiences and nature's changes. A healthy woman is capable of *processing* data. She recognizes that much data, social and personal, is contaminated and must be decoded for its valid meaning to be determined. In the processing, she sorts, assesses and analyzes, in order to determine the data's validity and whether the elements are helpful and constructive or hurtful and destructive to her. As her self awareness increases, she uses her own experiences, and analyses as the central criteria. The healthy woman is capable of *making decisions* based on her processing of data which promote survival and growth for herself in positive relationships with others and with the natural environment. The healthy woman is capable of *making judgements* about needs and goals as well as likely consequences in directing her behavior. The healthy woman is *aware of and uses her power* and energy in dealing with her self and her environment. The healthy woman is *knowledgeable* about herself, her own needs, goals, and ways to gather support as she acts on her commitment to her own and others' survival and development of self. Her commitments and analyses bring her to *challenge and change* that which can be changed within herself and her society, and to *learn to survive* that which cannot be changed. The healthy woman engages the contradictions between victim and agent, negotiating the social constraints and individual responsibility.

In contrast, the unhealthy woman does not have a woman's identity. She *distorts or questions* the validity of her own perceptions. She *uncritically accepts* the values and perceptions of others and denies responsibility for making decisions or taking actions. Instead, she follows imposed norms by internalizing others' views and acceding to their requests, or she withdraws, claiming and perhaps believing, incompetence, illness, or dependence. The unhealthy woman has denied or distorted her own self perceptions and needs. Often this leads to being hurt or severely damaged, but it always places her at risk. Her dependence also makes her unable to act in her own behalf or to gather support from others in challenging the demands of her hostile environment. The unhealthy woman does not engage the contradictions. She becomes a victim or a victimized agent for the power systems. She becomes disabled from health as she is defined by the power systems.

A woman who merely cloaks herself in feminism can be unhealthy, too. Doing the hard work of confronting the internalized messages, clarifying and strengthening one's own voice, analyzing the meaning of the data she receives, and making commitments to others and to change, are necessary for health. Feminism, if this work is not done, can become yet another power system presenting certain images and beliefs while selectively valuing and rewarding actions, roles and options. A woman is also at risk if she uses the movement as the focus of her uncritical dependence.

The unhealthy woman does not have a woman's identity and cannot join in sisterhood to gain affirmation and support, so critical in withstanding power systems' attempts to control. Nor has she the awareness and analytical ability to decode contaminated data. Instead, she believes internalized images, roles and options shaped by the power systems and accomodates to them. She cannot receive the valid data from her self, nor can she hear the voices of others or the environment, for the power system has distorted her perception. From inside the power system, the voices of self and others have been distorted, muted or silenced. Without the ability to more fully perceive, without the ability to decode and understand, without the contact with one's own and other voices, without the commitment to survive and change, and without the affirmation and support from other women in these shared burdens, the power systems' oppression of self, image, roles and options continue unchallenged. The unhealthy woman has not the awareness, support, opportunity or skills to engage the contradictions of social constraint and individual responsibility.

While women are victims of distorted data, discrimination and devaluation by power systems, and are damaged both socially and psychologically in this regard, we wish to avoid the simplistic conclusions that women are merely passive victims or that they are wholly to blame for their weaknesses or vulnerability. This issue is far more complex than that.

In our constructs of health, there is an overt attempt to remove the discussion from the victim/survivor or weak/own fault dichotomy. Women are victims, and the damage is both social and psychological. There is merit in the view that women are both victims and survivors. However, the victim/survivor view does overlook the fact that people are not passive, that there is agency, and there is responsibility to oneself. The opposing view of weak/own fault, seeing only agency, results in blaming the individual. Thus, it alleviates the necessity of questioning the power systems and allows the separation of self from others. It does this by denying the reality of social forces and their control of social conditions and resulting psychological status. Victim versus agent is too simplistic. The juncture of individual responsibility and social control is far more complex. The constructs of health proposed here follow from this juncture. In fact, women are oppressed. This oppression controls and manipulates their beliefs, actions, and psychological status. This is clear. However, women are not passive, and choose either to make the attempts to break out *or* to remain within their constraints. There is certainly great variability among individual women in the number and force of constraints, their psychological impact, and the resources available. Also, clear and important differences exist for women with respect to ethnicity, age, race and biology as well as life conditions, all of which limit choice. For each woman the harmful forces, resources, and psychological impacts are different. Choice is delimited. Attempts to break out entail serious risks and have little chance of complete success. Yet remaining within also entails further harmful restrictions and damage. The choices for women are often few and poor, and reside within endangered agents. Thus, this juncture of individual responsibility and social/economic/psychological constraint is complicated, uncertain, and risky.

The status of women and the discussions in the earlier chapters lead to a set of assumptions to which the definitions of power systems and health, and our model of feminist therapy are related. These assumptions are as follows: 1) Women as a gender are oppressed. 2) This oppression limits their ability to improve their social and economic conditions. 3) The oppression impacts negatively upon their psychological development and status. 4) Women as a gender have been denied their history, strengths and valid identity. They have been fragmented into sub-groups and alienated from one another. 5) Anti-female bias is predominant in values, views, rewards and decision making in the systems having power over the choices/options available to women. These systems include family, social, political, economic, health care, educational, and religious social structures. 6) Women as a gender are disadvantaged personally, interpersonally, socially, economically, and psychologically. 7) The inferior socio-economic status, constrained roles and options and relative powerlessness of women as a gender are critical and causative factors which must be given central consideration in responding to their mental health problems. 8) Therapeutic interventions intended to assist women in attaining and maintaining mental health must also address the power system environment in which they live.

Feminism can provide insight into the ways that women have learned to accept their devalued status, self-defeating and limited options, and to produce self-denying behaviors. In our model of feminist therapy, harmful adaptation is a developmental process evolving from social conditions and constraints imposed by the power systems. It considers the dependent status of women and its psychic link to their feelings of self-hate and hopelessness.

DESCRIPTION OF HARMFUL ADAPTATION

We describe the process by which women learn to accept dependency and to practice self-negating behaviors as that of harmful adaptation. We recognize that in adapting to the expectations and demands of power systems which discourage or punish women's independence, women are harmed. They are harmed because adaptation requires that they thwart their own development and growth, and deny their own views of themselves, their nature, skills and behaviors. Women are injured by adapting to and continuing to meet the needs of the power system.

Although most people are veterans in some manner of this process of "education," our examination of this method of instruction will focus on the ways it is used in our culture specifically to handicap females, to limit them to dependent behavior, and to destroy their self-esteem. We will also focus on how the casualties of this kind of training, the abused and self-hating women, are further harmed as they continue to serve the needs of the power systems. The process of harmful adaptation is developmental, repeated over and over from infancy through adulthood by nearly all the power systems in the social context. Some methods of instruction are as subtle as the mother's well-intentioned guidance of her daughter, while others are harsh and overt as in the physical force of rape. Sometimes this instruction is intentionally hurtful, and the goal of inducing helplessness and dependency in women is clearly articulated. More often, however, training in harmful adaptation comes about as part of the accepted role playing in the social drama of our culture.

There are obvious similarities between this harmful adaptation process and those processes used to initiate and train men for roles within fraternities and the military. But unlike these processes, there is no choice in seeking entry, no change of the harassment process in achieved membership and no awareness that the system is voluntary, time limited, and unique. Instead, for women the process is continual, widespread and presented as appropriate for women. Through a feminist analysis of female status and development, we are uncovering this largely unconscious social learning process and seeing its effects both systemically and on the lives of individual women. In order to understand women's health, one must consider not only the social sexism and power system abuse, but also how the restrictions, evaluations, exclusions and social message become internalized by women. Feminist analysis gives some understanding to the uniquely female; largely unconsciously internalization, the psychic link.

The process of harmful adaptation is illustrated in the following chart. The five stages of harmful adaptation are: humiliation, inculcation, retribution, conversion, and conscription. These represent a prototype of the power systems' dynamics and their effects upon women. The effects include both the woman's experience of the dynamic and the psychic link of its psychological impact. This prototype of the harmful adaptation process serves as the bridge between the dynamics of sexist and discriminatory power systems, and the mental health status of women within those systems. That is, it translates the social constraints and external forces to individual consciousness. The damage to women's images of their options, roles and values, as well as their potential to develop or maintain positive mental health, is clarified by this model of the translation of sexist discriminatory attitudes and practices, to women's personal experience, rewards and sense of self.

Though the chart leads to the impression that the five stages are the same for each woman and sequential, these are artifacts. The phases are overlapping and repetitive as well as variable in form and strength for each individual woman and cut across lines of socioeconomic level: race, culture, ethnicity, class, age, historical period and geographic region.

HUMILIATION

Humiliation is the experience of being reduced to a lowered position in one's own and others' perceptions. The purpose is to replace pride with humility through the consciousness of one's defects or shortcomings. Humiliation undercuts one's sense of worth and disables one from asserting one's own needs and ideas. Humiliation negates self-respect or blocks its development.

Humiliation can be experienced in many ways and to different degrees. It can be experienced through a sudden, single traumatizing event such as being physically overpowered, beaten or raped, or being verbally insulted, degraded or denounced. It also can be experienced as a slow accumulation of events such as being denied deserved rewards or privileges that are given to others, getting rewards

Harmful Adaptation Phase	Experience of	Behavior/Feeling
Humiliation	Being overpowered, exhausted, defeated, unable	Doubt, fear, self-hate, rage/shame, submission or withdrawal
Inculcation	Being taught "correct" behavior (behavior that won't be punished); being instructed in survival; being presented contaminated data	Reception of power system ideals, demands; anxiety/fear about ability to perform to standard; must obey rules; must secure protection and escape punishment; conflict between need to learn correct behavior and loss of self
Retribution	Being threatened with loss of rewards; punishment if correct behavior is not practiced; repressing or punishing opposing data and actions	Resignation; compliance with power systems' values and demands; anxiety/depression; self-hate; helplessness; hidden tension
Conversion	Accepting power system values and goals as own; accepting own state of dependency as good; distorted perception	Rejection or denial; repression of own goals, values and experience contrary to power system values, as bad, relief/hope, acceptance of inferior status and constrained nature; identification with aggressor, or reaction formation
Conscription	Serving as power system spokesperson and harmful adaptation trainer; justifying dependency as only natural and virtuous state for women; being complicitous with power systems	Apologetic, self-denying behavior used to ingratiate self to "superiors"; denial of health and worth of all non-dependent women; self-righteous presentation to power systems' values; feelings of anger, depression, self-hate for failure to reach power system ideal; sublimation and repression of independent self, wishes and visions; rigid denial of any values contrary to power systems

only if submissively practicing self-effacing behaviors, being chronically abused in situations such as incest and family violence, being the object of sexual harrassment, and being witness to the exploitation and trivialization of women in the media, advertising, and entertainment industries. For women, the humiliation experiences are a part of living within power systems as is the fact that women's humiliation experiences are usually dismissed as insignificant and their injuries denied. The social acceptance of devaluing attitudes and humiliating actions towards women suggests to women that such treatment is deserved. The more the humiliating experiences are related to the fact that the victim is female, the more a woman comes to self-hate or denial of her woman's identity. These factors lead to perception distortion for women. They come to perceive their lowered positions as accurate and themselves as unworthy or not real women. The affective concomitants are doubt about one's own abilities, shame for one's gender, lack of self-respect, indirect rage, and perhaps a denial of one's identity. Humiliation results in losing faith in oneself and devaluing one's gender. It places women in a vulnerable state because their experience is that they are not adequate to the task of living, not as valuable as others, and without the resources to survive alone in the world.

The vulnerable state resulting from humiliation leaves a woman without either pride in her gender or a sense of worth about herself. Thus she is open to the promises of assistance, and instruction related to what she should be and how she should behave. Humiliation establishes a compelling learning environment. The lessons are then taught in the inculcation phase.

INCULCATION

The lessons of the inculcation phase are presented to women who have been predisposed to learn as a result of humiliation. These lessons are taught both socially and interpersonally and result in internalized beliefs. The learning is enabled by the promised rewards of social approval, potential self-respect, and access to limited resources and protection, if specific behaviors and tasks are performed. The lessons differ among individual women and are

separated by age and life circumstance. However, there are three basic themes consistently taught and reinforced by the power systems
and their actors, with some ethnic, racial, cultural, and class variations. These themes are taught and reinforced in all the interlocking
power systems; opposing lessons are repressed. The ideal value images, appropriate roles, and possible options for women are so consistent and recurring across all power systems that women come to know
these themes by heart. That is, made vulnerable and then induced to
learn, they believe and internalize the themes. In the face of repressed
opposing information and reinforcement for the themes, they know
only that the themes are reality and that theme-consistent attitudes
and behaviors are regarded as right. Any opposing wishes that they
may experience, internally or externally are wrong, unnatural and
perhaps dangerous. A view of the world and women's nature and role
within it is being built upon contaminated data and through distorted, selective and ultimately disturbed perception.

The three themes are:

1) Positive valuing of male aggression;
2) Sex-linked dichotomization of human traits and abilities; and
3) Women's inferior status and properly dependent roles.

The Positive Valuing of Male Aggression

Male aggression, the seizing of control of people and situations,
taking over responsibility for making choices for others, competing
for and capturing positions of leadership, the active pursuit of
power, and using physical and intellectual abilities to win for self,
thereby limiting the alternatives of others, is presented by power systems as a demonstration of strength. This is the very strength required by a dependent woman in her protector; therefore it is
intended to be regarded by women as an attractive and desirable
trait. The threat involved in the dangerousness of male aggression is
also used to distance women from this source of power. The excesses
of male aggression which occur regularly in war, violent crime, com-
bative and "daredevil" sports, street fighting and spouse and child
abuse are not seen as evidence of basic flaws in the male character.
Nor are they perceived as reasons for aggression to be de-
emphasized in our culture, or as any form of discredit to the sex.

Instead, such excesses are regarded as indications of the reserves of strength which decent men must learn to hold back in social interaction, but which can be unleashed in the protection of themselves, their families and their country. In this way, the war movies' heroes and villains, the tales of famous outlaws and bad guys, the crime lords, the assassins in their battles with cops and spies, the bar room brawls and cowboy confrontations are all used as a celebration of the release of the aggressive strength of males. It serves as evidence of the correctness of male dominance in power systems and as a warning to women of the dangerousness of coming too near it, of coveting that power for themselves, or of doing anything other than submitting to it or avoiding it (Janeway, 1980).

Thus, women are given a double message: Be afraid of the power of aggression, yet seek it in a protector, since you cannot be aggressive as a female. Women are taught to accept hostility and dominating behavior as part of man's nature, and to be grateful for any restraint of this basic drive in relationships with them. Aggression against women is to be regarded as a necessary risk, much like the side effect of a powerful drug. Women are also taught that male aggression is properly harnessed if it is attached to society's plow of work and familial responsibility. And harnessing it is a dutiful civilizing function that women are expected to perform for society. They must perform it with caution, respecting the potential for violence. They must approach it indirectly through manipulation and suggestion. Women must never confront the male's power openly or attempt to negotiate the sharing of control by claiming strength of their own. That claim would challenge the second theme of inculcation, which is the dichotomization of human traits into sex-linked attributes and deficiencies. Women are also led to understand that they bear the responsibility for both the male's resentment at having to restrain his aggression within social convention, and for the degree of his success in doing so. The blame will be placed on the woman for a husband's uncontrolled drinking, a father's abuse, a son's delinquency, a boyfriend's irresponsibility. Even as strangers outside relationships, women must expect to shoulder the burden of male hostility. This hostility is variously explained, and excused, as the result of male fear that they again might develop the same intense childhood dependency which held them to their mothers

(Chordorow), and as the natural consequence of the repression of their basic drives in the service of society (Miller, 1976).

Many other sources reflect and reinforce the positive valuing of male aggression. Among these sources are the various entertainment media, television, sports, movies, and literature. We see popular approval for American aggression as in the invasion of Grenada, as well as continued respect and support for the military. Further evidence of this positive valuing of aggression is seen in the focus and selling of the news, and in the organization and inclusion criteria for history, politics, and economics. There is also the underlying assumption of dominant psychological paradigm in areas of motivation and human nature. These are a few of the structural and content impositions of male aggression on the American consciousness.

Dichotomization of Human Traits and Abilities

This theme further reinforces the need of women to depend on men through its arbitrary stance that human nature is split into mutually exclusive halves. It serves to define and implicitly regulate what one sex has and can do, and what the other sex lacks and cannot do. Power systems, historically male-dominated institutions, have set the norms according to male experience. Therefore, it is not surprising that, in the division of human traits, males get the positive traits denoting strength, reason and prowess which justifies their dominance, and females are assigned the negative traits, which justify their devalued, subordinate status. In her study of the ways in which "permanent inequality" of women is established, Miller (1976) states:

> Out of the total range of human possibility, the activities most highly valued in any particular culture will tend to be enclosed within the domain of the dominant group: less valued functions are relegated to the subordinate.

What better way to remove activities from the repertoire of subordinates than by denying them categorically by sexual definition the traits and abilities necessary to perform those acts?

Listed below are some of the traditionally sex-linked traits and abilities:

Male	Female
Wordly, concerned with important matters	Oriented to the home and family, concerned with trivial matters
Active	Passive
Sexually active/aggressor, sexually experienced	Sexually passive/resistor, sexually naive
Adventurous	Cautious
Strong, invulnerable	Weak, vulnerable
Brave	Fearful
Rational/Intellectual	Instinctive/Emotional
Independent/Leader	Dependent/Follower
Proud	Modest
Confrontive	Adaptive
Defensive	Nurturing
Explorer/Challenging	Caretaker/Accepting
Physically strong, hard, adept	Physically weak, soft, inept
Spiritual, holy, like God, blessed	Of the flesh, sinful, unlike God, cursed

This split of human traits and abilities also establishes an opposing, different operational structure to the definition of good and evil, of natural and unnatural, of sick and of well. Good men and virtuous women match the stated criteria; deviations from this natural dichotomy are bad and unhealthy.

Ignoring for a moment the conceptual incorrectness, the greatest danger in dichotomization is in the belief that such traits must be held exclusively, that there is a need for difference, separation and tension. This belief insists that for him to be strong, she must be weak; for him to be a man of intellect, she must be a woman of emotion; for him to be brave, she must be cowardly. Dichotomization declares that the world is either/or, separation and differences.

As long as there is acceptance of the current organization of society, and its male-female relationships of unequal power are desirable to power systems, and as long as the possibility of shared power is denied, the dichotomization of human traits and abilities into male positive and female negative will remain as given. The conclusion of inculcation is the instruction of women in the proper manner of deference which is required in the service they perform for their superiors. Of course, as liberal feminists and the Androgeny model (Kaplan and Sedney, 1980) argue, if the emphasis were positive mental health rather than the perpetuation of the social/economic/political-cultural status quo, then selected characteristics from each list would be combined into criteria essential to healthy human development.

Women's Inferior Status and Dependent Roles

Women learn from the cultural messages, institutional functioning, and interpersonal experiences, the contaminated data that aggression-seizing control, forcing choices, competing for and capturing leadership, and imposing physical and intellectual control for one's own end is the functional process and valued dynamic in our culture. Women also learn that the prerequisite abilities and traits are not seen to be appropriate or possible in women. The belief is that internalization of inferior status and dependent role is the only option for gaining protection, wise guidance and resources. To survive with minimized risk from aggression, to gain access to competence in knowledge and judgement, and to garner economic resources and social approval, women must accept their inferior status and secure a dependent role.

If a woman learns the first two themes, she believes in male aggression and sees it as evidence of the strength, intelligence, reason and correct power. She believes that she is incapable of these qualities and that her nature, appropriate role and value are in nurturing and supporting. She believes that to survive she must attach herself to a protector, that she has no alternative except the subordinate role in an unequal power relationship and its maintenance through flattery, pleasing, desirability, caretaking, ease-making, and collusion. If she chooses to resist the message of these themes, she may be excluded from the approval, rewards, protection and resources of the power systems, placing herself at risk of being seriously endangered.

The spokespersons of the power systems and of the messages of value images are either people and structures who have adapted to the demands of that system and serve it, or those who benefit from its works. The images they use to describe the woman most desired by that system reflect the systems' needs, rather than any reality about the nature of women. When those needs change, so does the image. Far from being the immutable truths that power systems insist they are, value images are never stable. They change with the changing demands on the system which holds them and uses them to meet its needs.

The psychological cost to women of the inculcation step of harmful adaptation is obvious. The inculcation message carried by the three themes is a no-win statement to women: Accept the fact that you are inferior and embrace it as your identity and meaning. Learn to accept contaminated data and perceive distortions of reality regarding self-concept, abilities and potential of women. Accede to shifting images and demands of power systems by behaving in self-negating ways which reinforce these beliefs for others and self. Learn to depend upon others for survival, further alienating oneself from one's strengths, and increasing the risk of failure. Janeway (1980) speaks eloquently of the pain of these conditions: "This excruciating despair is related to powerlessness, to the crushing belief that one is worthless, a creature whose feelings have no validity, whose actions produce no effects."

To the extent that a woman opposes the themes of the inculcation process and to the extent that she believes her own voice or those few others which counter the power systems, she is taking the risk of being trivialized, discounted or punished. Her protection and access to resources are endangered, and her power systems' rewards and approval are threatened. Psychologically she experiences anxiety, conflict and insecurity about her worth. If she behaves in overt opposition to the power system's standards and images, she is punished. The lesbian women in business are not promoted to middle management. The working mother is blamed for her child's difficulties in school. A woman who behaves with assertiveness and intelligence is told she will not catch a man. The angry or depressed woman who does not fulfill her service functions is labelled physically or mentally ill and encouraged to seek medical or psychological care. The woman caught in race and class discrimination and unable to support herself will receive little social welfare until she has children. Labels of selfish, lazy, bad mother, radical lesbian, sick, crazy, immoral and communist have strong negative psychological impact and are used by power systems to discourage women from the pursuit of goals not sanctioned by the systems.

Retribution

The shifting value images of inculcation can easily confuse women who are attempting to live up to these ideals of behavior and make them anxious about their ability to achieve congruence and thus please their power system superiors. The punishments described and demonstrated in the retribution phase further increase their sense of personal vulnerability to the point of panic. This stage of the harmful adaptation process is defined by the threats and punishments inflicted upon women who fail to live in accordance with the themes of inculcation. The retribution step re-identifies the unsympathetic enforcement function of power systems, after the more benevolent instruction and guidance function of inculcation.

The experience of punishment, whether threatened or performed, whether experienced directly upon oneself or indirectly through observation of actions taken against other women, provides an echo of the earlier humiliation phase of harmful adaptation. It causes an activation of women's memories of these events with reverberations of the pain of being overwhelmed, losing control, of being forced to submit to the will of another and of being denied their power to make choices for themselves.

The message of retribution is that to resist the themes of inculcation is to go against the will of all the powers that be, to flaunt one's claim of equality before God, Man and Nature, thus bringing down upon one's head the just punishments of the deity, society and biology. The punishments promised for such insubordination can be sufficiently severe to extinguish a woman's desire to continue behavior considered immoral, pathological and unnatural by power systems, and to increase the probability of her making more acceptable choices in the future. Retribution reminds women that submission can be forced upon them. It prepares them through fear, escalated to the point of exhaustion and resignation, to deny themselves the option of resisting the application of their inculcation learnings to their lives. The price of such resistance is set so high during retribution that few women feel they have adequate resources to meet it.

The goal of independence, of challenging the power system's restriction to inferior status and surviving, is portrayed as a prize only heroes can win, and in the dominant culture few female models exist to encourage women. If the burden of self-responsibility, of struggling against the power systems' insistent demands for dependency, becomes too great to take up and to bear, then the submission of self to the will of others can be seen as a welcome relief, a blessing. Retribution, strategically employed, can replace the dignity and hope of non-dependent persons with the shame and resignation of an acknowledged inferior, of one who becomes dependent upon the goodwill of another to survive.

The primary outcome, then, of the retribution stage is women's internalization of both the power systems' teachings contained within the inculcation material, and of the enforcement of the application of these principles in their lives. When this goal is achieved, women police themselves, and conform to the power systems' standards. The hallmarks of the retribution phase are the feelings of guilt, anxiety, worthlessness, and self-doubt. These feelings contribute to the efficient movement of these same women through the phases of conversion and conscription.

A secondary outcome of retribution is the isolation of women, discouraging the formation of a group of disadvantaged people who could develop the ability to provide support and protection for each other, and a possible challenge to the authority of power system superiors. The affiliation of women could offer them identity demanding equality, rather than as subordinates whose value, meaning and identity lie in their relationships to their superiors.

The mechanisms of retribution operating within the discriminatory social fabric and institutionalized bias against women in our culture are complex and interactive, making a women's success in "non-feminine" roles and structures unstable and very difficult to achieve. Lacking support from power systems, each woman builds her own, using her internal resources as well as her friends and mentors to defend against critical attack. The amount of psychic energy expended in these efforts often precludes other involvements and activities which would contribute to her development as a person. Even at this high cost, her success is not assured; she remains vulnerable to attack for her incongruence with the dependent, self-effacing feminine role model put forth by power systems. She may be charged with sleeping with her evaluator; stealing data for publication; being a token of affirmative action requirements; or having luck or sponsorship, but not the skills and abilities necessary to meet promotion standards; or of being too narrow in her interests and not possessing a personality attractive to clients and peers.

Discriminatory norms, pervasive devaluation, predicted or threatened punishment, labeling, banishment, and scapegoating are mechanisms of retribution which are used to discourage women from choosing nontraditional roles.

The personal costs of success for women are portrayed in negative characterizations presented by power systems: the iron bitch, the old maid, the super achiever who is an unfit mother, the competitive and castrating wife, the female executive headed for a nervous breakdown, the friendless and loveless woman at the top, the eccentric rich lady. These characterizations can be used to further discredit women who resist being restricted to dependent roles. Women who are incongruent with the images valued by power systems are judged and labeled. The noncompliant client in the health care system is defensive and counterdependent; in the educational system, the ambitious female student is an overachiever; the nontraditional woman is pictured in family systems as unfeminine, in religious systems as immoral, in criminal justice systems as deviant, suspect, or dangerous.

More overt punishments for serious violations of the norms of the dominant culture are banishment, the placing of women in custody or control of the legal system, the mental health system, the welfare system, the special education system, the unemployment compensation system, until they remediate their so-called deficiencies and practice appropriately compliant behavior.

Scapegoating, the assignment of responsibility to women for creating the problems of society, and bringing harm to themselves and other people, began with the stories of Eve, Pandora's box, and Helen of Troy, and continue in the present day. Mothers are blamed for their family member's mental health problems, wives for causing their husbands to drink or have heart attacks, daughters for seducing their fathers into incestuous relationships, women for bringing on their own rapes by their mode of dress of presence in inappropriate places. Presenting women as the cause for individual and societal problems distorts data, reinforces negative self images of women, and increases feelings of guilt, inducing women to conformity if they wish to avoid further social judgement and punishment.

A double bind is created for the woman who progresses this far in the harmful adaptation process. She has internalized the learnings of inculcation and is sufficiently convinced of her powerlessness to be willing to police her own actions and thoughts, both frightening and shaming herself out of noncompliance. She may appear well adjusted to her assumed role, properly socialized, well trained in making feminine behavior choices. Yet the internal conflict for a woman who is learning power system teachings creates tremendous cognitive dissonance for her. She is taught that she is privileged to be a woman, and also that as a woman she is naturally inferior and must therefore play subordinate roles. It is a "crazy-maker" message to be told that you must feel worth and value in being inferior, yet it is a familiar one, existing in many power systems.

Conversion and Conscription

Conversion, the next stage of the harmful adaptation process, combined with conscription as the conclusion of the process, offers a way to cope with the double bind message, a way to reduce the pain of the loss of self-respect and to resolve the cognitive dissonance of two incompatible lessons. Conversion allows a woman to embrace as a belief that inferior status is an opportunity for salvation rather than a fate to be despised. It allows her to be convinced that as a woman she is uniquely suited to a life of service to others, of finding the meaning of her life in her dedication to them, and that this ability, this selflessness, although perhaps not rewarded in the same ways as more selfish pursuits, will allow her to attain true peace of mind. It is true that, at least for awhile, this belief brings a sense of relief. She is removed; she can now see the present status of women as fortuitous. She has left the battleground for equal treatment with a conversion adjustment in perception, and has taken up cognitive residence in the world as she is told it should be. Her tranquility is disturbed, however, by the voices of other women who continue to point out the hardships and hurts they have suffered and who continue to work for change in their environments. The convert must then attempt to evangelize and conscript these women to the service of her cause in order to silence their voices of protest. This reduces her own whispers of discontent and sense of contradiction.

If retribution heightens the psychic pain of retaining a sense of self apart from power systems' value images, then conversion can be regarded as the anesthetic to take away that pain with the denial of self. By sacrificing her "selfishness," a woman becomes the perfect servant, a person with no needs, ambitions or identity of her own.

Conversion as a way of coping with restriction to inferior status not only reduces conflict but it also allows the mobilization of a woman's energy to meet the demands of the power systems.

Conscripting other women to the ranks of those who accept dependent relationships and inferior status as part of womanhood, as a virtue rather than a problem is a way for the convert to "prove" to herself the correctness of her belief and establish the approval of her power system superiors. The convert's belief is an effective coping mechanism for the fear, guilt and anxiety generated by the double bind of retribution. If, however, her new faith is all that holds together a broken spirit, a self-hating person concealed within a saint's demeanor, her own feelings of helplessness may show in the rigidity of her thinking, the self-righteousness of her defense of her behavior, and the desperation of her need to have others agree with her.

The convert, the victimized agent, provides invaluable assistance to the power systems whose teachings she reinforces. She conscripts new believers and helps in the administration of the harmful adaptation process itself, for her teachings, judgements and threats of punishment for those women who oppose her support of power system values are a part of the work of humiliation, inculcation, and retribution. As a spokesperson for power system ideals, she claims to represent what all decent women, those who are proud to be feminine, should want and believe.

The woman who is unable or unwilling to take the conversion step, who gets stuck and does not complete the harmful adaptation process, becomes paralyzed at the end of retribution, stuck within the painful double bind of self-hatred and hopelessness. These women are perhaps less "crazy" than those who are able to retreat to an altered state of perception through conversion. Yet they are in physical, intellectual, and emotional distress and are often the people who see themselves or who are seen by others as needing help. They may turn to friends, health professionals and family for support and for healing. Unable to deny their feelings, thoughts, ambitions and experiences, which they know are incongruent with power system values, they are at an impasse and may exhibit all the emotional and physical symptoms of stress, including episodes of anxiety/panic, phobia and depression. They may suffer from colitis, migraines, lower back pain, hyperventilation, high blood pressure; they may become drug or alcohol dependent.

The convert whose adaptive cognitive structures and repressed anxiety have wavered to the point that they no longer shield her from her feelings, may suffer the same symptoms silently. She denies her need for help because she is convinced that her unhappiness is a sign of failure. She believes that if she were truly good she would be happy, and since she is not, she is imperfect and deserves to bear her pain alone. However, if the rewards promised her by the power systems fail or are insufficient payment for the self sacrifice demanded of her, eventually the protection of her faith may fail. Since loyalty to the power systems' values demands a woman's contentment with her status and the roles expected of her, the unhappiness of a convert betrays her as an unbeliever. She is isolated from the faithful and has no way to cope with the pain she feels she deserves for being imperfect. Having completed the harmful adaptation process, she has learned to allow others to hurt her and has learned to be complicitous in damaging herself. Yet it is only when her pain incapacitates her in providing the service expected by power systems, that a woman will be considered to be in need of help. The assistance offered by the mental health establishment may further harm women. Conventional mental health judges both the results of the power system value images and resistance to them as pathological (Kaplan, 1983; Chesler, 1977). The woman reaching out to the mental health establishment for aid, is often met with a diagnosis to label her pain. The label does not reflect an awareness that the woman's loss of function could be the result of attempting to adapt or cope with the sexist social context, but instead indicates a deficiency within the woman herself. Labels such as hysterical, manipulative, weak ego, immature personality, depressive, passive-aggressive, eating disordered, or psychosomatic or anxiety disordered not only do not place causation in sexism, they do not even regard factors external to the person. Stereotypical sexist roles in social and family relations, economic dependency, imposed and learned dependency are not considered.

The social constraints and personal risk and damage stemming from the inferior status and harmful adaptation process are complex and interwoven, far more than we can discuss here. Instead, we indicated selected elements. We organized our illustration in pointing to the contaminated data produced, presented, and enforced for women in the social contexts through the messages, structure and functioning of the various power systems. The risks of conforming and the dangers of not conforming have been identified, as were the resulting psychologically distorted perceptions and damaged self. We also described interaction between the external forces and the individual impact on health. Our emphasis is the psychic link and the psychological development and status of women.

The social devaluation of women leads to their devaluation of self. Where men have generally lived out their roles in projects for expansion and conquest, women have lived out theirs through denying autonomy, being used by others and allowing themselves to become objects (Ascher, 1981). While not responsible for this, they are complicitous. Social organizations and functional structures within the social fabric are instrumental, controlling and damaging. The harmful adaptation process is a characterization of the interaction. It illustrates the psychic link. The internalization of the devalued status within anti-health social organizations, the process of making personal the external constraints, the psychological damage of discrimination and devaluation, and the hostile environments all have their effects on mental health. Because women have strengths, many are able to cope and to elude control by the harmful adaptation process. Varying degrees of harm and distress are the result of differences in conditions of oppression and internal resources.

In the next chapter, "Corrective Action and Health Maintenance," we will explore the task of providing assistance to the woman who is trying to heal her hurt and regain her health. We shall also examine the larger dimension of the problem, that of removing or reducing the elements of the harmful adaptation process within the environment of all women. As we tend the pain of the individual, we must attend to the society which creates, allows and encourages such injury to women.

If health, once attained, is to be maintained, new systems must be developed which support rather than discourage women's growth as self-determining, equal human beings. The key to constructive human institutions will not be found in present power systems. Miller (1976) comments that "major societal institutions are *not* founded on the tenet of helping others to develop." It must be found instead within the repository of strength and skills accumulated and passed on from mother to daughter, from sister to sister during the ages of struggle against the forces of repression. These new systems must arise out of a new community of women.

CHAPTER FIVE

CORRECTIVE ACTION AND HEALTH MAINTENANCE

FEMINIST therapy not only involves assisting women to undo the damage of harmful adaptation described in the previous chapter, but it also extends to confronting the attitudes and practices destructive to women in the environment. We call these two elements of the therapeutic process corrective action and health maintenance, and regard them as interdependent and parallel. Corrective action replaces a woman's shame and self-blame with a positive concept of self and self as a woman, supplying new information to counter the data contaminated by power system bias. The process builds women's skills and strengths so that they can be their own agents, negotiating with the persons and groups who have influence in their lives. Health maintenance exercises these new skills and strengths in collaboration with other women to change present power systems' destructive policies toward women and to build alternative structures which support and encourage women's growth and development. The following is a table of comparison which outlies the steps of corrective action and health maintenance in undoing the work of harmful adaptation, educating women to cope in new ways and to find new strategies for survival in a hostile environment rather than adapting themselves to limited and dependent roles.

The phases of corrective action and health maintenance are interrelated. During the corrective action segment of therapy, a woman learns to respond to herself, recognizes her own needs and goals as valid, and accepts herself as a woman in relation to the wide range of

Harmful Adaptation	Corrective Action	Health Maintenance
Humiliation Self shame, over- whelmed by other's strength	*Separation* Self discovery, Study of harmful adaptation environment	*Recognition* Pride in celebration of womanhood
Inculcation Invalidation of own experience, acceptance of others' values	*Validation* Validation of own thoughts and feelings even if incongruent with power systems' values, developing woman's identity	*Expression* Sharing of own experience and perception
Retribution Isolation from women and compliance with power systems' expectations under threat of reprisal	*Association* Finding acceptance in company of women with diverse values and experiences	*Cooperation* Development of interdependent working relationships with women
Conversion Denial of self responsibility, entrusting care of self to others' strength	*Authorization* Acceptance of responsibility for self; building own strength, woman's identity, articulate own goals	*Identification* Acknowledgement of bond of responsibility between all women, pooling of strengths
Conscription Presentation of subordinate roles, inferior status as only proper choice for women	*Negotiation* Interaction with power systems on own behalf to meet needs, goals; active resistance to harm, withdrawal if necessary	*Confrontation* Alliance with other women to work for change in systems or creating alternatives

Summary Purpose

Harmful Adaptation	Corrective Action	Health Maintenance
Internalization of externally imposed	Awareness of destructive elements	Discovery and development of a

devalued status and dependent roles, enforcing limitation of self and oppression of other women as power system agent. Passive, other directed	in women's environment which impede self determination and equality; preparation of self to challenge them in pursuing own goals; active, possessing psychological autonomy	community of women who can work together to change power systems so that human growth and individual freedom need not be sacrificed to achieve system's goals; proactive, social, economic, political interdependence

philosophical beliefs, political stances and lifestyles of the women she has come to know through her experience and her reading of feminist literature. Finally she commits herself to work on her own behalf in active negotiation in pursuit of her goals.

The parallel element of feminist therapy is a community building process for women confirming positive women's identity, encouraging acceptance and open expression of differences, and the development of cooperative methods of working for change. If corrective action can be seen as preparation of a woman to be her own agent, health maintenance combines her strength and agentry with those of other women to assemble the power base necessary to develop alternatives and change traditional systems which limit, devalue and abuse women.

As each step of corrective action and health maintenance is described, particular attention will be given to the requirements of both client and therapist in completing the work of that phase of therapy. The impact of the adoption of these concepts within present mental health provider organizations will be addressed in Chapter Seven.

Women come to corrective action with varying degrees of damage from their environments, and they have differing psychological as well as actual living needs. Also, women hold different religious, philosophical, and political beliefs, and use differing bases on which to judge value. Women will differ further in their goals for lifestyles, sexual orientations, as well as degrees and kinds of involvements. These differences are real and important. Acknowledging women's differences as well as their similaries is inherent within the steps of corrective action and health maintenance. There is no pressure, either explicit or implicit, to reduce women's diversity or achieve sameness.

Women Seek Therapy in Different Statuses

Women often come to corrective action in crisis. Others come not in crisis but with a specific problem which often is discovered to be more general and pervasive. Also, individual women have different skills, abilities, damage, and psychological needs requiring various helping strategies as well as amounts of time and support. Some women have such severe pathology, as discussed in Chapter Two, that they cannot function in or benefit from direct therapeutic use of this model.

Hence, this model with its conceptualization of steps and parallel segments is not to be considered a blueprint applied without awareness of real and important differences. Yet, it does capture a process important in healing women, based upon both the differences and the similarities among women in oppression and its psychic results.

SEPARATION

The first step of corrective action is that of separation. It assists women to see themselves as existing apart from the demands and needs of those around them, thus achieving the beginnings of psychic separation and individualization.

The difficulty of a woman's separation phase depends upon the degree of damage done to her by the harmful adaptation process. The woman whose concept of an independent self has been prevented or destroyed must literally find herself. She must allow herself to uncover and experience all her feelings and thoughts, even those incongruent with the power system values as reflected in the views of her family, friends, church authorities, superiors at work, or government officials. Although women may vary in the degree of their dependent attitudes and behavior and in the resistance they have offered to the process of harmful adaptation--and despite class, social and economic differences and related privileges they possess-- the task of separation remains the same. The symbiosis between each woman and the power systems influencing her must be broken.

The first stages of separation may be very difficult and frightening for a woman, for the helping person is asking her to step outside the world she knows, reality as she has learned to accept it. The possibility that this step may help her escape the pain she is experiencing may serve as a motivation to take the risk, but it is the therapist who is the prime encourager in a literal sense. The therapist must assist her to find the courage to begin to heal herself. The healing process, though fraught with feelings, is largely cognitive, an unlearning, a challenging of the assumptions about herself and about the nature of women which have constrained women as individuals and as a gender. In some crisis situations, particularly those having to do with violence, physical separation may be needed. Generally, cognitive separation is the goal of this phase. The disorientation risked in the disruption of one's sense of self shouldn't be underestimated, for the dimensions of the task make it a profound and anxiety producing event.

As a woman begins to examine the assumptions she has accepted about herself, she may experience feelings of discontent, conflict and anger, as these assumptions were promoted by people and institutions she trusted. Jessica Heriot and Kaplan et al (1983) have both published excellent articles explicating double binds for women from power systems and the necessity of anger as well as the centrality of feeling. Attending to the woman's emotions at this point legitimizes her and solidifies the therapeutic relationship.

Emotions as she experiences them become the information upon which begins the decontamination. Being a person who has been told what to feel and what she must not feel until her perceptions have become distorted, she now must learn to recognize her own data and her own experiences which are uncontaminated by the power systems bias. A variety of specific therapeutic techniques and approaches can be employed to provide assistance during separation and the beginning stages of self-discovery.

For example, a Gestalt therapy approach could be helpful in identifying interjects of the power systems and breaking through the woman's confluence with her environment, allowing her to experience herself as a "figure" instead of being the accomodating background to the needs of others whom she accepts as being more important than herself. Sex role analysis and cognitive restructuring coupled with reading of women's literature is helpful in the identification of the social structures and behaviors which tend to place women in a subordinate, inferior status. Behavioral therapy analysis may help to define the ways in which women have learned to restrict themselves to socially approved roles. Rational-Emotive therapy might assist in uncovering the irrational beliefs and the "I should" messages that control their choices. Values clarification exercises can assist women in sorting out what they think and feel from what they are expected to think and feel according to their socially prescribed role. Psychological analysis uncovering developmental experiences and psychic damage may be extremely important. Interventions during separation may involve various therapeutic styles, within the philosophical framework of feminism, which reinforce self-responsibility, self determination and equality. During the separation phase, a woman will see herself as acted upon in damaging ways through the power systems' training and use of her. The feminist viewpoint can help her to see herself as capable of moving from passive compliance with harmful limits to taking constructive action on her own behalf.

The feminist therapist serves as a guide in her client's self discovery and exploration, and moves to a consultant role later on as the client is involved in decision making. The therapist's ability to allow her client to be fully heard, to experience the power of listening, deep understanding and the intimacy of the total contact of two women, even momentarily, breaks through the client's isolation and aloneness to establish a personal connection. The counselor's skill and knowledge lie in discovery techniques, attending skills, promoting self awareness, articulating conflicts and fears, uncovering feelings and body messages, examining environmental damage to the self. The therapist can offer assistance in the separation phase of corrective action by examining external causation for internalized self blame, doubt, hate, and psychological symptoms. Within the context of an egalitarian relationship, the therapist seeks to meet the client's needs with appreciation of differences and client readiness. Most important at this stage, the therapist can also offer identification as a woman, a function which a man cannot perform. Women inculcated with power systems' values and norms may automatically perceive a man as a superior, quite apart from his own intentions or actions. She may reproduce the traditional male/female dynamics within the therapeutic relationship, stepping into another dominant/subordinate situation, thereby enlarging her confluence with her damaging environment rather than achieving a separation from it.

To achieve separation, then, is to step out of the power systems' constructs, assumptions, theories and prescribed behaviors for women, so that an examination can be made of the effect of the woman's environment on her growth and development as a self-directed person. In order to accomplish this, the classical structure of women to dominant superiors, experts, or authorities must be completely avoided. Instead, egalitarian relationships based upon the shared experience of being a woman is needed. The relationship between feminist therapist and client is one of equals. Each may have differing conditions of oppression, and be at different points in the process of healing and possess different kinds of knowledge. Both have essential pieces to a puzzle that has no predetermined right solution. Together they cooperate and share in the process of healing, emphasizing the client's examined and self-directed activities. It is a non-judgemental atmosphere, for the client herself is the expert; only she can determine what is right and wrong, good and bad for herself. In this relationship between peers, the client holds the key to unlock her own experiences, once devalued, trialized, ignored and oppressed, and now considered relevant data.

The study of the harmful adaptation process itself is an important part of the separation stage, as it identifies the power systems' methods of instruction and the process by which they obtain behavioral compliance with their goals. When a woman can make the very power systems which limited and controlled her the objects of study, she can gain some distance from them. She can lessen the hold that the power systems have had on her through their teachings, by beginning to examine and decode their messages, identifying the needs, goals, and uses for women that underlie the values that the power systems wish her to accept as her own. As she contrasts the promised rewards with the actual social, economic and psychological consequences of the chronic self denial and dependence that are recommended to her as a lifestyle, she starts the critical analysis that can protect her from the internalization of external prescriptions and norms. She sees that there is no objective reality to the power systems' claims of her inferiority as a woman; oppression, not nature, is her problem.

The study of harmful adaptation also provides a structure for women to credit themselves with the survival skills and the creative coping mechanisms they have used for generations under oppression as a gender. Many of women's special strengths and qualities such as intuitiveness, emotionality, and sensitivity have been trivialized and devalued in their societies, while these same strengths and qualities are used to benefit the systems women serve as subordinates. During the separation stage, these qualities are recognized not as feminine flaws, but as abilities and strengths that make women able to face the trauma of separation. This study also provides a way for a woman to see herself, not as a victim but as a service provider to power systems which have encouraged the dependency which now places her at risk. Examination of the harmful adaptation process brings woman away from focusing on feelings of defeat, isolation and helplessness. They see power systems' messages as self serving propaganda, not as reality, and recognize that they have internalized these messages as truths. By decoding the messages and regarding them as protective of the system rather than of women, they can change the effect of these messages upon their behavior, attitudes, and self image.

A woman's examination of the process through which she was hurt and learned to limit and to punish herself is upsetting and painful. She may experience grief at the death of her fantasy of dependency on a benevolent caretaker who would and could be responsible for the fulfillment of her every need and for taking control of her life. The death of this hope and its exposure as myth is often mourned. The fear involved in admitting feelings and thoughts incongruent with power systems' values and norms is significant. As her sense of self was dependent upon compliance with serving in subordinate roles and behaving in a power system approved dependent manner, these fears may surface with corresponding intensity, and impede further growth. Sensitive psychological work attending to the psychic link of oppression, self hate, doubt, fear, is called for as are the real life survival needs of money, child care, etc. Therefore, the next phase of corrective action, that of validation, must overlap at the point that these feelings and thoughts begin to emerge. Meaningful support must be provided for the woman who is discovering new and sometimes disturbing data about herself, and facing fears and needs. Validation of herself in the acceptance of the client's self discovery by the therapist, can reduce the fear involved in the experience of incongruence with traditionally approved values and role models. This phase of separation is a long and difficult process involving the achievement of psychic distance from former assumptions and the recognition of one's own voice.

VALIDATION

During the separation phase of corrective action, the client begins the process of psychically removing herself from the dominance of power systems. She acknowledges the pain she is experiencing and learns to explore her own feelings and values. She is able to analyze the process by which she came to be hurt, to doubt, to deny and to punish herself. In the phase of validation, she is affirmed and supported as she explores her emerging identity. This is a time of great vulnerability for the client. In individual therapy, the therapist may be the only validation of the client's new information about herself at this point in the corrective action process. The therapist is modeling self acceptance for the client as well as demonstrating how one woman provides non-judgemental validation of another woman's experience as real and true for her.

This phase of corrective action confronts the invalidation of the person that took place during the inculcation phase of harmful adaptation when women learned to discount themselves and to accept the values of power system authorities while disregarding their personal experiences. As the client moves toward self-acceptance, she may be working with a group of women engaged in feminist therapy who are willing to share their experiences and analyses, and to practice validation of self and of others in a supportive setting.

Some women come to feminist therapy with a good understanding of the dynamics of power systems' manipulation of women and with supportive connections with other women. Others may resist feminist interpretations and be fearful of emotionally close contact with women. One of the skills of the therapist must be an accurate sense of timing. The process of corrective action must be based on the readiness of each woman, and it must be appropriate to her goals. Feminist therapy must never impose a system of beliefs on its clients or push them into situations they do not wish to experience. If it does, then feminist therapy becomes one more power system which attempts to limit and control women. It abandons its healing function and becomes oppressive. For example, if a woman comes into therapy in order to deal with an eating problem, depression or anxiety, her stated need, the presenting problem, should be addressed at once. If, as she begins to unlearn self-negation or other self-destructive behaviors, she starts to examine how she learned them, then elements of the corrective action process may become appropriate intervention strategies. Corrective action in feminist therapy seeks to free women from external criteria, to achieve an integrated awareness of the social, economic and psychological realities of being a woman as defined by the client. It seeks to uncover and develop the woman's unique nature. No prescribed program can achieve this. Although each phase of corrective action and health maintenance is described in general terms here, the application of the therapy model will vary for each client as it must be based upon her specific needs, goals and readiness.

During the validation phase, if the client responds to the support of her therapist and other women by becoming more comfortable with her self discovery and less fearful that she will be punished for incongruence with traditional values, she will have broken part of the hold that the power systems had on her. She will no longer depend exclusively upon biased external sources of information to help her make life choices. She can now report and accept her own insights, and trust her own perceptions. She understands that other truths exist which conflict with those she was taught during inculcation and that there are alternatives available which power systems deny exist. Validation of the data she is uncovering may change her perception of the world so much that it seems upside down. She may feel that she is going crazy, feel disoriented because she lacks the guidelines imposed by power systems, but actually she is going *sane*.

Part of the client's responsibility towards the end of the validation phase is to extend herself beyond the therapeutic relationship and make contact with women's lives which lie outside her immediate experience. There are literary and artistic works, group activities and personal expressions of women who, like herself, are moving past old restrictions, questioning their identity, their ties to traditional roles and their loyalty to power system goals. These "outside" experiences are helpful in the preparation of a client for the next phase of corrective action, that of association.

Therapeutic actions that are useful and appropriate during the validation phase of corrective action include core facilitative conditions, attending skills, body work, psychosynthesis, and further cognitive restructuring. Suggesting readings for the client and discussing their connection with the therapeutic process can assist the client in recognizing that others have shared her experiences and worked through similar issues. Facilitation of affect, both verbal and nonverbal, assists the client in the free expression of her feelings. The suggestion of alternative interpretations and the use of personal disclosure by the therapist, present the client with the opportunity to analyze new information for its significance to her situation. Journal writing, fantasy, articulation of the client's strengths and skills, and goal clarification may be helpful in furthering the client's self-exploration and assuring her active participation in negotiating the therapeutic contract. Sue Kirk (1983) and Greenspan (1983) offer differing but strong and valuable discussion of psychological intervention.

ASSOCIATION

The therapeutic alliance between a woman in pain and her helper must be a microcosm of a larger healing community in order to progress, and it must connect with this larger community if the individual's progress is to be reflected in her environment.

Association with other women, both the physical getting together for social or task purposes and the establishment of psychological contact between or among women, is necessary to break down the barriers, the isolation, the fear of differences and mistrust built up during the retribution phase of harmful adaptation. During validation, women start to allow themselves to experience their feelings and thoughts without censoring out those incongruent with power system messages. They begin to build data bases that are less contaminated by power systems biases and which contain more information helpful to the formation of individual goals, satisfaction of their perceived needs and the maintenance of their health and well being. They no longer have to distort their perception of their needs to fit the roles prescribed by the power systems.

They start to regard their own thoughts and feelings as being as valid as those of their power system superiors. Without validation and the support of association, such data would be too dangerous, too guilt provoking for most women to assimilate. Without association, each woman must keep her new truths, her new world of experience, to herself, her helper and perhaps a few trusted friends. Her perceptions may be clearer, but without the risk of seeking out and trusting other women through association, the truth has not yet set her free. Her isolation would continue to keep her in a relatively powerless position. Association brings with it the new knowledge that she is not alone in her experience, that though she is unique, many of her thoughts and feelings and experiences have been shared by countless other women crossing the lines of culture, class, race, and even time. The association of women, the empathy and support and help, the open sharing of self-validating people, can help them to more fully recognize the important of their grievances and their power as a group. The threats of retribution are designed to prevent such phenomena. All associations of women are in danger of attack by power systems. Such associations are perceived by those systems to have the potential to usurp power, change present structures, or threaten the systems themselves. Association of women often must take place over objection, ridicule and disapproval of power system superiors. Contemptuous references to "you girls getting together" implies that only juvenile, unimportant action could come from such a group. Retribution tactics may be used to interfere with the psychological connection of association as well. Charges of lesbianism, incompetence, irresponsibility to family, and selfishness are not uncommonly experienced. Association moves women to look past status and role to acknowledge a basic commonality of purpose and a shared respect despite differences. Association makes the connection that the retribution phase of harmful adaptation seeks to discourage and punish.

The woman who becomes concerned about the economic and social plight of women in developing countries and who sees that the way other women are treated is important to her life becomes aware of the fact that, if any person is abased or despised because she is a woman, then all women, no matter what class, race culture, or subgroup are also indicted. The recognition of the bond of sexual identity supercedes all other divisions. For the woman in feminist therapy, association with other women, either through joining a group, participating in a community, or by the psychological connection of concern and involvement in the lives of other women, is a step of high risk. She so recently felt herself to be helpless, and avoided conflict with the power systems by acting in such a way as to win approval or avoid punishment. She now goes against the teachings of the themes of the inculcation phase of harmful adaptation by offering support and encouragement to other women and accepting the same from them, by forming interdependent relationships with equals instead of the power system approved subordinate-to-dominant relationships suitable for maintaining the status quo. The information she hears and shares challenges the inculcation themes. Association risks both punishment and great rewards, for sharing with other women can be shocking, hurtful and healing. It is shocking in that the awareness of the suffering, the injustice, and the abuse of women across cultures and classes engenders rage at the power systems that allow or cause such conditions to exist. It is hurtful as one experiences the pain of empathy, feels compassion, and shares the injury of other women. There is also the sting of complicity, of recognizing that, by providing service to the power system, one has been a part of such injury. Association is healing as it assists one to accept and forgive oneself, to see women's problems as society's engendered in an effort to perpetuate the inequality of the sexes. Women feel badly about themselves because they are treated badly and often blamed for their own abuse. Through association, women can come to see being female as positive and good, not as an admission of inferiority. They accept their womanness and recognize that there are problems to address and barriers to be broken down as well as strengths to explore and use.

Association risks great punishments for it exposes a woman to the disapproval of power systems she previously tried to appease with "feminine" behavior. She is now held responsible not only for her own acts of rebellion against her restrictions but is guilty by association for any infractions by members of her group. She is viewed with suspicion for seeking female rather than male support. Women who had been compliant before association and whose behavior changes from submissive to assertive will be accused of aggression, of willful destruction of the fabric of society, of moral inadequacies, implied sexual deviance and pathology for their efforts to question the status quo. Divorce, loss of child custody, loss of employment, and economic deprivation may be the consequences of association, for repression and discrimination of women is the rule rather than the exception. Women are not protected, but penalized by the systems upon which they are dependent. The rage which surfaces with this realization of trust betrayed often surprises a woman who felt she was well adjusted to her role in life. The consequences of the client's changes must be analyzed thoroughly in therapy.

The pain of association is the sharing of awareness, of promises not kept, of trust betrayed or rewards denied, of the manipulative exploitation of the individual, and of the contempt of the abilities of women as a group that makes such manipulation possible.

The hurt of experiencing competition, dislike and distrust from other women has been reinforced in the isolation fostered by the retribution phase of harmful adaptation, and the fear of rejection must be overcome in building the trust required in the association phase of corrective action.

As a woman acknowledges another woman's pain, she comes to respect her own. As she is able to show compassion for other women, so she becomes able to risk feeling their empathy for her. As she learns to value other women, so she learns not to devalue herself. As she is able to accept women as whole persons, so she can reject the image of herself as a flawed creation, an inferior person, a second class citizen. As she is able to hear other women's experiences of oppression, so she gains a clearer analysis of the effects of sexism.

The corrective action phases of separation, validation, and association restore to women what the harmful adaptation phases of humiliation, inculcation, and retribution would take away: the awareness of systematic injustice toward and exploitation of females, a sense of inherent personal value not dependent on role or function, and a realization of women's potential. This is accomplished by expanding a woman's consciousness beyond her individual struggle where it is easy to capitulate to dependent status, so that she sees she is involved in the struggles of women's liberation from power system control. She realizes then that she is not alone, and that the outcome of her individual battle and those of other women she knows are important to the betterment of the situation of all women. Together they can accomplish what no one of them can do individually. Her separation from the psychic domination of power systems, her validation of self and association with other women is also important to her sense of herself as being worthwhile, creative, and competent. She knows her strengths and feels self respect in her struggles with uncovering her damage. She experiences anger and its useful motivation as well as the empathy, support and connection of sisterhood. She is aware of both her residual psychological damage and the consequences of potential behavior and actions.

In order to assist the woman in feminist therapy, attention should be given to the elements that contribute to the positive association experience. For maximal sharing and building of trust and communication, the following characteristics are required:

1. Non-judgemental acceptance of differences. Individuals may disagree on issues, values, beliefs and still respect each other and even hold each other in affectionate regard.
2. Openness to feelings. Unpopular feelings don't have to be denied to gain membership. There are no restrictions to role behavior.
3. Conflict acknowledgement and management. Disagreements are not denied but dealt with in such a way as to retain all parties in the group.
4. Non-hierarchical structure. Everyone is accepted as an adult and relationships are interdependent, equal to equal, cooperative. Shared leadership is a function of the group.

On the other end of the continuum, for the most negative experience of association, one that prevents or destroys connections between women, the elements which support the harmful adaptation process are:

1. Judgement criteria for acceptance based on assumption of what is good/evil, right/wrong, good/bad, feminine/masculine, with praise for compliance and punishment for non-compliance.
2. Restriction to feelings and behavior deemed to be appropriate for

females with the expression of inappropriate alternatives resulting in rejection and exclusion from the group.

3. Denial of conflict, as conflict is regarded as aggressive and forbidden to women. Surface "niceness" with underlying hostility will be found to be the actual role.
4. Hierarchical structures where women are in subordinate roles in auxilliary groups designed to support the work of power system superiors without any input into decision making.

Feminist therapy can and should help groups of women learn to function in positive ways. Basic group dynamics, including shared leadership concepts, confrontation and encounter techniques, feedback and specificity are often needed learning for women during the association phase.

The counselor also must assist her client as she confronts her resistances and fears, helping the woman restructure new beliefs and evaluate behaviors while gaining further insight into herself and other women. Various personal issues will evolve for the women during association around psychological dynamics, and unsolved problems from her own past history as well, concerning skill deficiencies which require behavior practice and/or change. These issues are appropriate to the individual counseling relationship. Also, each woman needs to learn during the association phase of corrective action to assess the positive and negative potential of her association opportunities so that she can make her choices based on the best chance for personal growth and support. The feminist therapist should be prepared to offer guidance, training and assistance in this process. The pull of association is powerful, and women are particularly vulnerable to placing others before themselves. Therapists can help women to achieve a balance of time and energy in their commitment to self and other women by learning to monitor personal needs and goals.

Groups from which women can derive the benefits of association do not necessarily need to share a feminist orientation. If the characteristics of positive association are present, membership in the local parent-teacher association may be as helpful as participation in a consciousness raising group. Similarly, a group which is described as feminist or woman centered may be a negative association experience for women if they are judged according to rigid criteria and are restricted to expected behavior.

Certain topics of discussion are particularly relevant to the women's movement, and may assist in building meaningful association relationships. They include the study of human development, social organization and violence against women, the analysis of women's service functions, the objectification of women and oppression, consideration of issues of private and public equality, and the exploration of personal creativity. Concern with humanizing social structures and communicating with frankness regarding the functioning of one's body, as well as one's emotions and sexuality are a part of a feminist orientation (Miller, 1976). Additionally, specific topics and life conditions such as eating disorders, the welfare system, age, race, mothering, are beneficial for individual clients with these concerns and for others to increase their awareness of diversity.

AUTHORIZATION

Association with other women assists the client in affirming herself, and in accepting her value as a person. Shared experiences of women during the association phase help the client put her own problems in the context of power systems' oppression of women. Once she is assured that her difficulties are not evidence that she is crazy, wrong or unworthy, but are held in common by many women in our culture, she is ready to authorize herself to be her own agent, to prepare to advocate on her own behalf. This authorization of herself to be responsible for her life choices is diametrically opposed to the surrender of self to the direction of others required in the conversion step of harmful adaptation.

It is very important that each woman examine her resources and assess her skills and strengths accurately to determine if they are sufficient to reach the goals she has set for herself. If they are not, then her skill deficiencies must be identified and plans made to correct these deficiencies through additional skill training.

The authorization phase is one of preparing the women with

information, knowledge, and skills to recontact the power systems in her environment during the last step of corrective action, that of negotiation. The assessment, skill building and preparation of the client must be thorough and accurate or we are confronted with the ethical dilemma of putting a vulnerable person at risk.

The assistance of males who are trained in feminist therapy or who are at least philosophically attuned to the goals of feminism (i.e., self autonomy, sexual equality, empowerment of women, ending discrimination and oppression of women) may be useful during this phase of corrective action. Males as helping persons during the earlier phases of corrective action are problematic because their presence may trigger the trained responses of dependency and submission in the women, and they cannot participate in women's identification. After a client has worked through the separation, validation and association phases, she is able to take a new stance in her relationship to power systems. As males predominate in the superior positions of such power systems as the family, education, politics and industry, a woman who wishes to build the skills necessary to negotiate with power systems' authorities will need first to practice these new behaviors with men in a therapeutic setting. In this relatively safe environment, she will be able to gain experience in developing egalitarian and non-manipulative working relationships with males and practice assertive communication skills before moving to the high risk interactions with men in authority in her environment. For the last two phases of corrective action, those of authorization and negotiation, male involvement can be useful in preparation of the woman for survival and growth in her world of male dominated power systems.

Skill building appropriate to the authorization phase may include formal training such as completing high school, further college education, apprenticeship programs or government sponsored skill training for unemployed persons. Skills can be developed in specialized counseling, in listening and communication and assertiveness training. Working with a speech therapist, developing a collective household for child care and financial needs, or forming a network with other women facing similar situations are often useful activities. For the female athlete or performer, it could be finding the right coach or teacher to develop her talent, or the right agent to help her to market it. Preparation for the negotiation phase could include consultations with teachers, mentors and role models, as well. Advocacy techniques to use in dealing with the social services and legal establishment are particularly important for some clients to develop. Any activity which will increase a woman's resources to deal with her problems and achieve her objectives can be a part of the authorization phase.

For example, a client who must overcome her anxiety about learning to drive in order to get to work might use this opportunity to take drivers' training instruction, to learn how a car works and how to handle emergency situations, and to develop sufficient expertise to select and arrange financing for an automobile. Therapy specific to weight loss, substance abuse, stress and phobic reactions might also be a part of removing barriers to maximal functioning of a woman in her environment.

Similarly, the authorization phase may be used to define and further test the client's decisions regarding lifestyle and/or work orientation by interviewing other women who have made these choices. Clarification of the client's values, needs, wants and motivations, and discussion of the implications for herself and for others of potential choices is necessary at this stage. Value conflicts and personal compromises between indvidual style or preference and real world requirements may arise around issues such as business and professional ethics, the commitment of one's energies to achieve financial security and status, or the wearing of traditional restrictive feminine clothing necessary for acceptance in certain settings.

During the authorization phase, the feminist therapist should be prepared to assist the client to find goal directed resources, to probe the realities and consequences of her choices and to re-examine her values in light of her plans. The therapist's role in authorization becomes that of a consultant and resource person as the client acts for herself in accord with her consciousness, her values and her developing skills. Experienced in life planning, realistic assessment, value clarification, and negotiation strategies the therapist can be quite useful at this time. This stage also includes a review of the client's process of corrective action, her new perspecives, skills and commitments, as well as the areas where the client is vulnerable to self defeating behavior choices. The therapist must also attend to the possible need for additional psychological work, continuous support and analysis, as the client faces the concrete responsibilities of the next phase of corrective action.

NEGOTIATION

The culmination of the corrective action process is the negotiation phase. It is toward its successful completion that the preparation of the other phases of therapy have been made, for it is during negotiation that each woman tests out the effectiveness of feminist therapy in assisting her to actively pursue her goals. In order to be successful, she must have undone the work of harmful adaptation. The self hating, self doubting woman whose direction and meaning came from the services she provided to others rather than from within herself must be left in the past. The self negating qualities of harmful adaptation training must have been transformed through corrective action to self enhancing abilities and attitudes. The movement expected in the corrective action process of therapy can be summarized as:

from self hate	to self respect
from dependence on others	to self responsibility and psychological autonomy
from perception of self as weak, helpless, unskilled, and alone	to perception of self as strong, skilled, motivated, and having the support of peers

If the preparation of the client has been complete, she reenters the environment as a person capable of choosing her own behavior, assessing risks, and planning strategies to accomplish her goals. She is aware of the dangers of dealing with the social forces of oppression and is in a better position to know which power systems she can reenter and whether she can change the roles she wishes to play in them. The support she has acquired through the validation and association phases is as important as the skills she developed during authorization, as skills alone will not sustain a woman in negotiation with power systems. As she leans to survive failure and defeat, and to grow as a nondependent, self determining person, she will need the reinforcement of other women who are participating in the same struggle.

The negotiation phase allows the client to move from the base of support, skill building and consultation acquired during authorization to direct interaction with the power system with which she is in contact. Perhaps within the health system, she has moved from being a passive recipient of service to an active, responsive and inquiring part of her health care team. Within the legal system, she could be working out a child custody agreement, investigating her rights as a consumer or addressing discrimination or sexual harrassment problems. In business or industry, she might be negotiating for a raise in salary or a promotion, or advocating better working conditions. Within her family environment, she may be developing a marriage contract which divides responsibilities equitably. The degree of confrontation and conflict management called for varies in each task; however, the basic guidelines for negotiation remain the same. The client must be able to state her requirements clearly, be certain of her goals, of what she wants to gain and how much she can afford to lose. She must be able to make decisions and plan effective strategy to meet her needs, and to evaluate her progress and analyze the cost to herself. As she practices negotiation behaviors, she needs to learn to assess the timing required to be effective, when to push an advantage, mobilize support, compromise, or retreat. She needs to be able to manage her emotions during the process and to deal with the feelings of those persons on the other side of negotiations effectively. She must also be prepared to lose and survive.

She must become a sophisticated agent for herself, within the social constraints. Quite different from the woman who passively hoped that she would be cared for by the power system superiors in control of her life, the woman who negotiates in her own behalf is making positive changes for herself, not trusting her fate to anothers' sense of fairness.

The therapist's responsibility while the client is practicing her negotiation skills is to serve as consultant, available upon the client's request. Activities that can be helpful during the negotiation phase include assisting the client in reviewing, processing, and evaluating interactions and in replanning strategy. The client may require support and feedback as well as the presence of a trusted person with whom to share both triumphs and defeats. The therapist and/or peer group may provide these services.

Once the client has learned effective negotiation and self advocacy with the power systems in her environment, she will have undone her own harmful adaptation. She may retain a few psychic scars, some vulnerabilities and the need to stay vigilant against being pulled into the self negating cycle again.

She has become a healthy person in an unhealthy environment. Her task now is to begin to confront the power systems' oppression of women and to work toward elimination of it through the process of health maintenance.

HEALTH MAINTENANCE

The process of corrective action is one of healing the hurt of women within feminist therapeutic relationships. Its goal is to undo the psychic link from oppression, generate analysis of oppression, create support, firm women's positive identity, build skills and strengths sufficient for each woman to lay claim to what she needs and wants and to work toward achieving it. The corrective action process is women's agentry. The process of health maintenance is challenging the social constraints for women. Both are necessary for health. Health maintenance seeks to change those structures, dynamics, and conditions which oppress and harm women.

The phases of the health maintenance process mobilize and focus women's skills toward the confrontation of elements of sexist oppression in their culture. Health maintenance is the antithesis of the process of harmful adaptation which denies the worth and strength of women as a gender and seeks to reduce to insignificance the influence women may have in the world in which they live. The preparation for the confrontation of power system sexism is the building of community among women who are self confident and aware of the elements in society hostile to them.

Feminist therapists need to be active members of the health maintenance community for several reasons: to safeguard their own health, rights and opportunities; to demonstrate egalitarian working relationships for their clients; and to live out the principles of feminism, devoting a part of their lives to work toward the improved status of all women.

This community of individuals must overcome differences and bond together to work for change, drawing from the strength and resources of all its members. In order to challenge the legitimacy of the powerful, the community must be able to withdraw its consent to be governed in denial of the myth of its own inferiority (Janeway, 1980).

The phases of recognition and expression celebrate past and present accomplishments of women, generating a group pride and sense of history. The cooperation and identification phases are developmental as the diverse community of women must evolve ways of working together which enhance the growth of the individual while building a cohesiveness and a sense of purpose within the group so that its members can find continued support, maintain their connections with women and work to change hostile structures and dynamics in their environments. These groups are not separate from corrective action: undoing, healing and change are continuous activities. While many women in the groups will have already confronted their harmful adaptation, they need continued support. Also, these groups provide the arenas for some of the learning for the sisters in the process of corrective action. These groups exist in organizations of women professionals, networking in human services, women's alternative social and economic collectives, political action groups, associations for women artists and performers, in support and study groups. Their existence in alternative women's cultures and within power systems are numerous. Too often, at present, these groups exist as separate threads which must be joined together in community and woven into the social fabric if a new, healthy design is to exist for women and to transform society.

While experiences in alternative women's communities provide some insights and troublesome features; and the beginning of women's community within the structures of the dominant social structures hold promise, our experience with feminist egalitarian social structures which support women, encourage their positive health, and are committed to change sexist structures and practice, is limited. The experience of freedom from sexist limitations is largely unknown. Arieti (1976), in his study of cultures which inhibit or enhance human creativity, concluded that "although the creative process is an intrapsychic phenomenon, it is part of an open system. The magic synthesis does not occur without input from the external world and it is greatly facilitated by a proper climate or milieau." For this reason, he held that disparity of creative achievement between men and women reflected "the extent and degree to which women have been mistreated by society" and predicted that the lifting of restrictions will prove to be an incentive to the creativity of women as well as other oppressed minorities. This is not to say that the principles are not clear nor that many lessons have not been learned. Feminism, its principles and history, as well as contemporary strides and achievements, provide example and analysis of the kinds of community and transformations which must occur if women's health is to be attained and maintained.

We can only imagine social structure and economic organizations that do not limit or harm women. However, we are beginning to experience the potential for interdisciplinary change, the development of women's cultures, the blossoming of creativity and the connectedness of women demanding change in the feminist community.

In the following descriptions, we will explore the attitudes and activities of each phase of the health maintenance process and relate them to the processes of corrective action and harmful adaptation. The implications of this extension of therapeutic responsibility into the development of new health-producing social structures and political activism will be discussed in the last two chapters.

Recognition

Similar to the search for roots of the black pride/black power movement, the recognition step involves the investigation of the history of leadership and contributions of women that have been forgotten or devalued by the dominant culture and of the chronicle of women's suffering and oppression that has been denied, concealed, or dismissed. Racial and ethnic minorities are strengthened by the collective memory, the recital of the stories of their heroes. Their striving for justice serve as a reminder to survivors of the need to band together and maintain their identity and commitment to work for freedom.

Women are beginning to discover and acknowledge the shared history which overrides the divisions of class, race and ethnicity. This discovery is of great importance, for it immediately changes the conceptual environment of women. Instead of seeing themselves as a class of subordinate beings reinforced by the dependent roles in which they are cast by the power systems they serve, they begin to perceive themselves as sharing a heritage of greatness and courage with other women.

The essence of the recognition phase, like that of each step of health maintenance, is within the group experience. The individual's recognition of women's history and heritage is a powerful experience, but when that experience is shared among a community of women it can be the catalyst to growth. The group participates in the unfolding of a new truth, in the discovery of the power of the sex whose strength has been denied by the dominant culture. In giving tribute to women who overcome the restrictions of their societies to make their presence felt in the drama of human affairs, they acknowledge the potential of every member of their sex.

The recognition phase of the health maintenance process can provide data and experiences which are helpful to a woman in the separation phase of corrective action. As she separates herself from power systems' messages of who she is, she needs new information, uncontaminated by power systems' demands to help her discover herself. The recognition phase can provide a place to being to construct a new definition of womanhood.

Activities which are helpful during the recognition phase would include reading of women's history and the philosophical and spiritual reflections of women, the accounts of the holders of folk wisdom, healers and midwives, and the persecution in past cultures. The study of the artistic and scientific contributions of women, the investigation of family legends, genealogy, taking oral histories, holding discussion groups on different topics and issues pertaining to women's heritage are a few of the ways in which such material might be explored and shared.

This recognition of women's history, oppression, survival, strength, damage, and uniqueness provides, along with expression, the energy for struggle and the sensitive committment to women.

Expression

Sometimes we learn from our study of the past not just the fact that a certain woman lived and accomplished a specific goal, but we are able to respond to her personal experiences and expressions in her writing, her art or her music, and we are able in this way to make a connection between our existence and hers. As we reflect on her work and react to it, the past becomes present, her thoughts and feelings have life in our consciousness. As the works of women past and present are shared publicly, women are able to explore themselves through each others' eyes. The image of the creator in our culture has been male, as the vast majority of persons gaining recognition for their work were male. The women who served as the audience for the creative works of males saw themselves portrayed in many guises: the muse, the model, the bitch, the earth mother, the seductress, all the characters which serve as contrast and background to male lives. For women to see themselves in the creative work of women as the subject rather than the object, foreground instead of background, protagonist rather than antagonist, is a unique experience of seeing the world as they are used to perceiving it turned inside out.

Importance is granted to endeavors previously regarded as trivial. We are able to see in the domestic arts the pent-up energy of women-centuries, and recognize the quiltmakers, embroiderers, weavers, potters, and all the practitioners of home crafts as artists who transcended the restrictions of the merely necessary to achieve the beautiful. An event like Judy Chicago's *The Dinner Party* celebrates the multiplicity of women's shared creative experiences. It can challenge women not to accord rank from great to small, but to encompass, to acknowledge themselves through the work and play of all women. Personal expressions and reflections of women's lives become a celebration of community and the discovery of the creator in every woman.

As we begin to regard art and literature, music, dance, and drama as media for the communication of the experiences of female human beings as well as males, the reflections of the human drama will show us a truer reality. Women's expression will not only give back to women a clearer picture of themselves, it will add by bringing other viewpoints to bear on human issues, new dimension and depth, a new perspective to the old cyclopian dominant male vision.

Innovations of women in the socio/political arena, new methodologies, the assignment of new priorities, developing concepts and different interpretations in government, education, academic research, military and industry as well as within families, assert a female based reality which also challenges the established male view.

As women learn to question the inculcation messages of harmful adaptation, and learn to trust their own truths through the corrective action process of validation, the expression phase of health maintenance becomes a natural outlet. Expression is a demonstration of uniqueness, the handprint of identity, a personal statement outside the restrictive roles and devaluating messages in the dominant society. Activities which assist women's participation in this phase include experiences of appreciating the expressions of other women and the sharing of their own through journal writing, stories, poetry, and drama, the visual arts and dance, as well as more academic expressions of research and analysis. They are also demonstrated in the collective structures and modes of functioning in feminist groups.

Whether a theater performance or participation in the unfolding drama of a consciousness raising group, the accomplishment is similar in that it reflects the continuing discovery of unexplored areas, ideas, relationships, the widening of life, the creation of a new self-made reality.

This new reality, if shared outside the community of women, may conflict with the world view of the dominant culture, however, and any criticism or threat to existing systems of power will be attacked and discredited by those groups who wish to maintain the status quo. Therefore, members of a community must be able to work together to provide protection and support for the expression of its members.

Cooperation

The development of interdependent task relationships within a community of women that is committed to the health and full participation of its members stands in stark contrast to the retribution phase of harmful adaptation which isolates women from each other under threat of reprisal by power systems. The degree of success of this phase of the health maintenance process will directly affect the ability of the community to confront and correct sexist oppression within the power system environment, for it is here that women combine their skills and strengths to work for each other. The practice of affiliative skills, the maintenance of human connections, the encouragement of the growth and development of persons have long been relegated, as trivial concerns, to women by the power systems of the dominant culture (Miller, 1976). Women are taught during the harmful adaptation process to use these skills in isolation from each other to benefit the systems they serve. In the cooperative phase, women learn to use them in caring for each other and in building a community that values these concerns. The challenge of the collaborative approach is in the ability of dissimilar groups to work toward a mutually beneficial outcome, and to develop new structures and dynamics rather than to resort to the competitive approach which declares winners and losers, haves and have nots.

It is vitally important during the cooperation phase to master conflict management techniques and shared leadership functions in order to empower all segments of the community of women and to implement egalitarian principles of self government. It is here that the internal division of the community of women must be acknowledged and overcome in commitment to the whole if a truly open system is to be established. Skill building activities of the cooperation phase can be as formal as special task forces providing alternative social services, dealing with issues such as violence against women, or as informal as a backpacking camping trip, and as unstructured as the bonds of friendship which can bring individuals through periods of grief and personal crisis. Training in group dynamics is especially helpful during this phase of health maintenance. Women in feminist therapy who are moving through the corrective action process may take advantage of the cooperative health maintenance community to experience the acceptance of association with other women. The activities and social structures of the health maintenance process serve as a resource to the feminist therapist and her client and as a model of the interdependence required in the maintenance of a nurturing protective community. For women involved with health maintenance, support, power, commitment and vision will be generated in their development of cooperation, and the structures and dynamics will foster it.

Identification

This phase of the health maintenance process builds upon the cooperative efforts of the previous phase, as the identification phase assists women in acknowledging their responsibility to their gender as well as to themselves. If the recognition phase of health maintenance corresponds to the black pride of the Afro-American movement, so identification is the equivalent of the "Black is Beautiful" concept. Each woman must accept herself as female, a condition like being black, which sets her apart from the white male superiors in most of our culture's power systems and makes positions of power harder to achieve. She must recognize that her sex is still her base of strength, her connection to the generations before her and to her sisters. Identification brings the realization that what women bring to their world is unique, that in many cases the skills they possess have not been tried, and that their strengths have been devalued and untested.

It is the female experience which challenges the accepted knowledge of male normed institutions and says that knowledge is incomplete and biased. Identification, like the step of authorization in corrective action, is a time of preparation for the conflict of negotiation and confrontation, preparation to assume more control over life choices, and to secure the possibility of self direction for all women.

There are many celebrations of sisterhood: Friendships, women's festivals and conventions, networks of women and business partnerships are opportunities for the identification of women as resources to each other. The positive self-regard of women during the identification phase is reflected in their respect for the wisdom and experience of other women. It is in contrast to the self-negation of the conversion step of harmful adaptations. The perception is of oneself as helpless and of other women as competitors for the protection of men. Along with cooperation, identification empowers women to challenge and seek to change those attitudes, practices and beliefs, as well as those structures which devalue and harm women and constrain them from their creativity.

Confrontation is individual self-responsibility enlarged to an inter-system level, raised to reason for being, a cause. As in the corrective action process, a woman authorizes herself as her own agent and prepares herself to negotiate with power systems in her own behalf; so, a woman in the confrontation phase of health maintenance commits herself to the goal of protecting and working for the betterment of society as a whole. Thus, women move into an arena previously occupied only by males, one of making the world a better place, of doing something to improve the lot of humankind. At the confrontation phase, women take on the moral responsibility of global goals.

The behaviors of the confrontation phase of health maintenance are the opposite of the self-denial and scapegoating of other women common to the conscription phase of harmful adaptation. They are assertive and collective, speaking clearly of the needs of women and with the voices of many women committed to each others' welfare. Confrontation can take place only when women have acknowledged their interdependence and forged their community, and are able to rejoice in being women, rather than to see in that condition the rejection and devaluation of their culture.

Just as surely as unionization precedes collective bargaining, so the community building phases of health maintenance must precede its final step, that of the confrontation of the elements of sexist oppression within the power systems which have influence over women's lives.

Confrontation as we speak of it here is systems advocacy. It occurs at the decision and policy making level of power systems, and challenges the hierarchical structure by the assertion of equality. It may be union demand of management to meet its responsibility for damaging the systems of nature, a petition to the house of bishops for an end to the exclusion of women from the priesthood of the church, a class action discrimination suit against a business or industry, or a group of welfare mothers demanding legislative policy changes.

Together the processes of corrective action and health maintenance combine to defeat the harmful adaptation of women to dependent, damaging roles and structures in society. Corrective action is taken on behalf of the individual during feminist therapy, and health maintenance is accomplished through empowerment and community building of a disadvantaged group. Therapy without the potential for changing the harmful elements of the environment is at best a temporary effort, healing only to place at risk and liable to hurt again. Therapy in a hostile environment is a sophisticated form of torture, for it keeps the person in pain alive, in full knowledge that further abuse will follow the therapeutic interventions. Corrective action heals the individual; health maintenance supports her health and works to change a hostile, unhealthy environment.

Organizing to improve and change the environment is ineffective unless the elements hostile to the self determination and equal treatment of women are identified and mechanisms to undo the damage they have caused are developed. The process of harmful adaptation must be fully understood by those women who combine their energies to improve the opportunities for women. They must be armed with the knowledge of how women are taught to be, think and act, and are complicitous in social constraint, and armed with the knowledge of the actions and experiences effective in assisting women to gain agentry in their lives. It is this knowledge combined with cooperative efforts of women that will lead to social institutions based on the equality of their members, not on the debasement of one race, sex, ethnic group or social or economic class in order to benefit another. The principle of equality, if realized within systems of power, would bring about a profound change in all aspects of society and its functional values, including the maintenance of health.

Mental health is no exception. It must require its training, functions, policy and workers to articulate the psychic link of oppression and commit itself to changing the hostile environment with its special psychological focus upon human development, psychological implications, facilitative interventions, individual needs and changing dynamics. Mental health has an important and rather unique role to play in joining with others committed to changing the damaging aspects in the social fabric, cultural customs and institutional organization to growth promoting. Defined by health, both systems and their psychic links must be changed to become supportive, healing and growthful. This model of feminist therapy is a move in that direction. It integrates much of the former work into a model of therapeutic effort which, compelled by feminist principles, direct attention to the individual, her support and agentry, and the cultural and institutional forces in her own and society's environment. It demands change at all these levels.

In the next two chapters, we will explore the impact upon the present mental health care system of our model of feminist therapy, the metamorphosis required to begin to develop the capacity for corrective action intervention, and the community necessary for the establishment of health maintenance support functions.

CHAPTER SIX

THE IMPACT OF FEMINIST THERAPIES
ON TRAINING

TRADITIONAL TRAINING PROGRAMS

IN order to understand the unique properties of a feminist therapy
training program and the special problems which will be encoun-
tered in establishing such a program, first it is useful to look briefly
at the objectives, structure, curriculum, and training methods of
typical traditional mental health training programs.

As might be assumed, the traditional training programs are
shaped by the same forces that determine the nature of the professions themselves. The state, professional and academic bodies that
control the mental health professions by establishing licensure and
certification criteria, setting federal grant and insurance requirements, and presenting guidelines for professional practice, inevitably impose their underlying theoretical and political constructs on
the mental health profession. Control over training is crucial to
maintaining the status quo within the professions, because the training programs are responsible for producing individuals who will
adopt the professional goals and methods prescribed by the dominant model. The national professional associations establish stringent and very specific criteria for training program approval, and
elaborate evaluation processes for identifying programs that meet
those criteria.

Thus, a training program which teaches a theory and practice of
mental health that conflict with the dominant model will, in all prob-

ability, not be endorsed by the professional associations, and will be refused accreditation. Students trained in unaccredited programs will not gain certification and licensure, and therefore will not be able to enter and infuse new perspectives into the profession.

The dominant model of the mental health professions and their training programs is the medical model. It is this model which determines the ideology and sets the politics. The medical model in the mental health professions presents assumptive beliefs as facts; interacts with cultural norms, social policy and government regulations; informs mental health policy and practice; awards expert status; establishes entry and membership; legitimizes knowledge and establishes validity of methods of discovering new information. In short, the medical model controls, directly and indirectly, the content, process and outcome of mental health in its corpus of knowledge, its standards, and its practitioners and practice.

The medical model has resulted from a number of historical events combining to form a powerful paradigm. The rise of reason in the Renaissance, empiricism and its protege, the scientific methods, hierarchical structures and professionalism along with their contribution to differential power and expert status, achievements through general acceptance and effectiveness in physical medicine, the influence of Freud, Behaviorism and psychoactive medication, and religious, and social beliefs and policies of charity are but a few of the historical variables in the evolution of the medical model. The historical development, the far-reaching influence and the widespread acceptance of the medical model and its larger paradigm are critically important factors in understanding the dominant model in mental health. However, the degree of articulation of the medical model in the mental health professions is sharply delimited.

Because of its long development period, integral functioning and widespread acceptance, as well as the absence of well-developed and contrasting models, the medical model is very difficult to see clearly. Both the nature and scope are so much a part of functioning and belief systems of mental health, that they have become like reality. The arbitrariness of the assumptions, the constraints on knowledge and the shaping of relationships and policies have been all but forgotten. In traditional mental health, a medical model, its paradigm and its related dynamics have become the rarely questioned, dominant mode of belief and functioning.

The medical model in mental health is usually narrowly described as a set of assumptions about human nature, growth and development, mental illness and its causes as well as treatments aimed at remediation of mental illness. Paradigmatic and political dimensions, validation of knowledge, legitimacy of methods, institutional and litigous power are not generally considered or discussed. However, these are indeed potent variables in a systematic analysis of traditional mental health and highly relevant to a discussion of mental health training. Price, Lange, Szasz, Albee, Tennov, Chesler, Weisstien, and Greenspan, among too few others, do engage some of these issues.

Focusing here, narrowly upon the medical model as it underlies assumptions of mental health and remediation of it, is task enough. The medical model as currently conceived includes the following aspects: (1) A dynamic perspective of intra-psychic structure and processes, allowing for both trauma from external events and neuro-chemical, physiological deviations; (2) A nosological system which classifies mental illness and communicates it through the formal diagnostic language of the American Psychiatric Association; (3) An attention to vocational and interpersonal adequacy influenced by both sex-role ascription and the development of various therapeutic modalities including psychoanalysis, psychotherapy, family therapy, crisis intervention and relationship therapy; (4) Assessment procedures which include mental status evaluations (psychiatric), objective and projective personality tests (psychology) and case histories (social work); (5) A diagnostic and treatment procedure which reinforces the formal expert power relationship of the professional to the patient; (6) A variety of strategies for treatment which include not only insight, but also behavioral change and manipulation through chemical/electrical means as well as social, vocational and cognitive remediation; (7) A claim of apolitical conformity with dominant social norms as essential judgement of mental health; (8) A focus on the individual which excludes external factors except to assist or reinforce compliance with accepted norms; (9) A goal of conformity to social standards, not uniqueness; (10) Significant deviation from social constructions of thought and behavior is judged pathological; (11) Based on power, not on experience; (12) A monolithic criterion of white middle class western male culture.

These twelve characteristics of the medical model, though not inclusive, are indeed descriptive of the functional reality of the dominant model in mental health. It can be argued that the rise to a dominant position of the model has been beneficial for more enlightened and humane concepts and practices of mental health have been developed. When viewed historically, certainly the medical model is superior to former notions of God's punishment, and practices are better than those Dix fought against. Even today, in cases of severe pathology (as in manic depression or schizophrenia) the medical model serves well.

However, the unquestioned use of this model of mental health is clearly inappropriate for the entirety of mental health. The limits of the medical model are its blindness to factors of class, race, sex, its apolitical facade, its acceptance of white middle class sex-role ascribed norms and social order, and its labeling of differences as deviance. If extreme enough, pathology makes it a subtle yet powerful status-quo reinforcer. The dominance of the medical model in mental health does not capture the reality of mental health. Other views are needed to challenge its dominance. A single view is inappropriate to the complexity of mental health. The medical model has been important historically and continues to have importance with severe pathology. Yet its very dominance has obfuscated its inappropriateness for all of mental health. Mental health is a larger phenomenon. Forcing it into the medical model is narrow and dangerous.

STRUCTURE

Because the theory and modes of practice of the various traditional mental health fields, social work, psychiatry, psychology, are all based on the same theoretical model and controlled by bodies whose aim is to perpetuate the status quo, the professionally accredited training programs associated with these fields share several basic characteristics.

One such fundamental similarity is overall program structure, one aspect of which is the institutional setting in which the training occurs. With the occasional exception of social work, all training for the mental health professions occurs at the graduate level. Graduate training programs must answer to many masters. They are accountable to the university which specifies curriculum and program requirements, to the State Department of Education whose approval is necessary if the program is to be eligible to award degrees, and, somewhat less directly, yet no less importantly, to accrediting standards of professional associations. Therefore, the nature and organizational structure of a professional training program is under the control not of the faculty which is directly responsible for providing the training, but of groups external to the program itself, groups in whose interest it is to inculcate dominant social structures, and beliefs as well as status.

A consequence of this institutional control of the training programs is that the programs tend to become rigid and resistant to change. A program which is subject to the complex and entrenched regulations of the university, the state, and the professional associations, cannot quickly or easily change its structure or content in response to developments in the knowledge base of the field.

So the training programs associated with the various mental health fields are similar in their institutional environments. All are dominated by a complex of forces which work together to impose a traditional model of mental health on the professions.

Similarly, faculty are selected, evaluated, retained and promoted as the personnel in academic training programs on the basis of standards which promote the dominant institutionalized norms. Performances in publications, professional and university services and teaching are the typical criteria. In universities of status, excellence in teaching is not enough; while publications and committee performance are frequently enough to achieve selection and promotion. Patronage and sponsorship are often fundamental elements of committee appointment and membership. Publication frequently involves variables which include language style, paradigmatic compliance, and topic acceptability as much as the reliability and validity of the research or the logical arguments in an article. Hence the major criteria for personnel selection and promotion reinforce the continuation of conformity to the dominant institutionalized practices and beliefs.

Evaluation of students being trained in traditional programs also reinforce these same dominant norms. Students' academic performances are graded by faculty who are successfully institutionalized. The faculty makes the assignments and then judges the completion of the work. Rarely are criteria for grades articulated. The faculty member makes a practiced, yet arbitrary, sole judgement on the student's work. Open discussion of the evaluation of the strengths and weaknesses of the student is not provided. If discussion of the evaluation occurs, it is because of student initiation. As often happens in this type of power relationship, intimidation may be a potent force.

Clinical skills evaluation is often more specific and communicated. Yet there are strong elements of judgement based on conformity with dominant practices and exclusion of thorough assessment. For example, evaluations do not address the student's unique strengths nor creative forms of assistance to clients. Case management involving community action and facilitating linkages with alternative services are irrelevant to the evaluations. Yet the appropriate usage (acceptance of and compliance with) of supervision and agency policy are central features of most clinical performance evaluations.

Even in the initial selection of trainees for admission to graduate study in traditional programs, these same institutionalized habits and beliefs are stressed.

Selection of trainees in traditional mental health programs is commonly based on a rather rigid, narrow set of criteria, including scores on standardized tests, undergraduate grade point average, undergraduate course work and major, and publications. Prior experience in the field is occasionally considered in the selection process. In some programs, it is even a meaningful variable. However, the relative plethora of inexperienced trainees contrasts sharply with the dearth of mature, experienced trainees in the resulting selection of candidates in traditional training programs in mental health.

This discussion of the structure of traditional training programs has focused upon the systematic functioning of institutional practices and norms. Any consistent program must function through methods integrated with its beliefs and ideology. Hence the important thing is not as much the systematic application of dominant norms as the question of whether these lead to exclusion of important variables in the training process of the future practitioners of mental health. The central and critical question is one of competence.

CURRICULUM

Another consequence of the institutional control over the training programs is a similarity in content and process across the mental health disciplines in professionally accredited training programs.

Faculty are accorded expert status by their positions within the university structure and through their power over students. Within the parameters required and approved by the university, state and professional accreditation agencies, the faculty make the decisions. Through committees, individually, or as an entire departmental body, they decide which potential students are admitted, they set the number, kinds and performance level in courses. They require, write and judge examinations. They sponsor and support certain students through graduate and teaching assistantships and prize internships. They influence the selection of a research topic and control its development. They differentially interact with students, offering some co-authorship and not others, and further offer employment information/sponsorship and friendship of varying degrees. Traditional academic training programs in mental health are closed systems. Within the boundaries set by institutionalized control, the faculty have the power. An important basis of students' successful negotiation of this academic training experience is their degree of compliance and usefulness.

The major forms of training for students are inculcation of the power dynamics inherent in this hierarchical, closed system and passive absorption of current and historical beliefs. Creativity, radical critique, and choice are extremely limited. A student may choose one accepted theoretical orientation over another, say behaviorism over neo-analysis, but psychosynthesis would not be tolerated as a choice. One may critique the psychopharmacological literature for placebo effect or over-medication, but not with a thesis that medication itself is an inappropriate treatment intervention. Paradigmatic assumptions and current beliefs are treated as fundamental truths.

The student who challenges these is adjudged ignorant, in need of educating or inappropriate for further training and retention.

Were this process of training demonstrated to be the most effective, or the paradigmatic assumptions and current beliefs shown to be truth, then the process and knowledge constraints of training would be more justified. However, such claims cannot be made.

Clearly there must be criteria, knowledgeable people making decisions and mechanisms for evaluating the development of students. Then, too, there must be provisions for students to learn the corpus of knowledge in the discipline. The central questions such as competence in the earlier section, are found to be permeable systems, power relationships and knowledge.

As in the case of program structure, concepts, research methodology, and modes of practice taught in the training programs reflect the view of human nature and the "normative criteria" of mental health implicit in the dominant medical model. With differences in emphasis but not in fundamental concept, the training programs all teach the same basic personality theory. They also discuss such influencing factors contingent to the formal personality theory as family patterns, cognitive functioning, biological factors and genetic predisposition. The personality theory is generally an overview of existing common theories with substantial attention to psychodynamic approaches.

An emphasis on a diagnostic and treatment view, based upon psychopathology and assessment, is imposed on the professions and thus on the training programs by the dominant model. Similarly, attention to such narrow methods of intervention as therapy, psychotropic medication and the effective utilization of social mechanisms such as the legal, educational, and welfare systems are common across the programs. A basic issue related to intervention, treated in all mental health training programs, is the nature of the professional relationship between therapist and client, including transference, trust-building, and the therapists' diagnostic and treatment functions.

Two areas which differ slightly in discipline yet are common across them, are research and literature, and history. While each discipline presents its own history and body of literature, the history is interactive, and cross discipline literature is frequent.

Many training programs also include a survey of traditional human service agencies. The survey usually covers each agency's purpose, client services and requirements, structure, and methods of making contacts and referrals.

Finally, a common concern for the role of the professional runs throughout the professions. This concern, which may be treated in formal academic courses, supervision seminars, or professional colloquiums, encompasses such issues as ethics, legislation, accountability, and work settings.

As mentioned above, because the institutional entrenchment and dominance of the controlling bodies works to perpetuate the status quo, the traditional curriculum is often resistant to change and is incapable of timely response to significant developments in the field. For example, community psychology/psychiatry and consultation are two areas which have become important aspects of mental health practice, as evidenced by the growing literature in both fields, and by the flourishing of independent training programs such as National Training Labs and the Harvard Lab in Community Psychiatry. Moreover, the Comprehensive Mental Health Act requires that mental health centers seeking federal funding have consultation and education services which stem directly from community psychology and consultation.

However, despite the substantial evidence of the importance of consultation and community psychology/psychiatry within the mental health fields, many approved programs in social work, psychiatry, counseling, and psychology do not offer courses in these areas. Further, there is certainly no systematic effort to integrate the teaching of knowledge and skill required for proficiency in these areas into the curriculum. Most traditional mental health training programs are still geared to training individual therapists who work alone or in therapeutic teams to treat the mental illness or an individual. For the most part, these programs do not prepare their students to be professional change agents, policy makers, or preventive health workers— roles which are integral to the practice of consultation and education and community psychology/psychiatry. The training programs, entrenched in the dominant model, have not adopted the broad perspective of social and political analysis which is becoming vital to the effective practice of mental health in the field.

CLINICAL TRAINING PROGRAMS

The clinical training components of the various mental health training programs share much more in their similarities than in their differences. Outstanding in their sameness are the two aspects of graduate practice and supervision. Training in and practice of mental health is progressive. Under slightly different labels, the first stage is observation of professional activity and interaction with direct service professionals. The second step in the process is limited practice of professional skills including direct service with clients/patients. It is at this step that students receive selected case loads, co-lead groups, and are assisted in performing the other treatment and administrative functions in the service settings. In time, frequently associated with formal advancement in their academic programs, the students move to the final stage. Variously labeled advanced field work, internship, residency, are performed by the student trainees; these are fully professional functions, with supervision from experienced professionals in the service setting.

This sequential training pattern serves many ends. It provides the student with a graduated and assisted process of learning professional functions, a task which might be otherwise overwhelming. It serves as a protection for clients whose service needs would suffer were it not for the assistance and supervision rendered to the student in providing service. Finally, the process assures that students are inculcated thoroughly with behaviors, perspectives, and policies of the dominant model of mental health. Student-trainees are taught, assisted, and supervised in conforming to the conceptualizations, treatment methods, professional practices, and policies of traditional mental health. Indeed, agency supervisors are chosen on the basis of their conformity and skill in the dominant medical model, and as with the faculty in the university, become role models and standard-setters for students. Students model their ideas of professional practice and knowledge on their supervisors; hence, faculty and professional therapists, the personnel in graduate training, become the key to the attainment of an image about how professionals work and conduct themselves.

The second aspect similar across mental health training programs is supervision. Student-trainees may and in fact do learn skills from various people, but their supervisors are licensed or certified professionals in the same disciplines as the student-trainees. Experienced professionals thoroughly familiar with the setting are selected as supervisors by the hierarchy of the setting, and by university staff. Aside from agency regulations, personal and interpersonal dynamics, competence and conformity are preponderant factors in the selection of supervisors. The approved supervisors and the approved training sites provide traditional forms of mental health practice. Thus, in all the mental health professions, supervision (the vital bridge between academic training and practice in the field) and the agency itself, tend to reinforce rather than weaken the influence of the dominant medical model. As discussed earlier, structured evaluation forms, serving as communication from the supervisor back to the degree granting university, are designed to assess the students' attainment of clinical skills and attitudes relevant to the dominant model.

The similarities in clinical training components across mental health training programs illustrated here by introduction to clinical practice and supervision, as well as mechanisms of agency approval and evaluations, all reflect the systematic influence of the dominant model of mental health.

Traditional training in mental health has a number of striking similarities across disciplines. The training programs are highly developed and the components integrated. They are strong and reflect the interlocking influence of the state, the mental health professional associations, direct service agencies and universities. They also demonstrate the systematic impact of adherence to one dominant model of mental health.

FEMINIST TRAINING PROGRAM

The training of feminist therapists cannot effectively occur within this traditional configuration, both because the power structure which dominates the profession is fundamentally anti-feminist, and because the dominant model cannot accomodate the concepts and modes of practice which are developing to meet the unique psychological needs of women.

The concept of multi-leveled sexism is difficult to comprehend, yet its full comprehension is essential to the development of a feminist training program. An understanding of the many levels of sexism impacting upon the lives of women must be one of the primary goals of feminism and thus of a feminist mental health training program. While critically important, it is not enough to merely understand the attitudinal and structural existence of devaluation and of discrimination against women. Surely sex-role ascription and its use in personal interactions and social structures is important and its understanding an accomplishment. And to understand the cause of pathology as external, resting on social structure and conditions, and not primarily the weakness of the client, is indeed an achievement. Yet this is only one of the many levels of sexism. The other levels of sexism must also be understood, and their understanding must direct the development of a feminist training program.

The psychological impact of sexism upon women is one of those levels. Fear of accomplishment in male roles and fear of non-accomplishment in female roles, poor self-concepts, self-doubt, difficulty in autonomy and depression stemming from blocked anger, fear and self-hate are but some of the psychological phenomena for women resulting from sexism. These and others are thoroughly discussed in the Psychology of Women and popular literature. They, too, must be an integral part of the curriculum of a feminist training program.

At another level, knowledge is controlled through sexism. Only empirical or rational modes of knowing are legitimized in the male-dominated process of discovering, developing, evaluating, validating, disseminating and communicating knowledge. Each of these functions is complex. Their discussion, while fascinating, is beyond the scope of this chapter. The point here is that sexism functions on the levels of knowledge production, validation and communication. Limited modes of knowing and male dominated production and dissemination vehicles control data so thoroughly that alternative ways of knowing, and ideas not acceptable to the status quo are nearly totally repressed. Alternative ways of knowing, intuition, artistic sensitivity, personal-transpersonal insight, are distrusted or denied, resulting in neophyte development, no validation, and frequent retribution. Similarly, ideas and information which challenge the status quo are discounted, ridiculed, and not infrequently punished. This control of knowledge is crippling. These limits imposed on ways of knowing and even on the content of knowledge, as well as the repression of alternatives, are a result of sexism in the discovery/ production, validation, and dissemination of knowledge. This must be understood and moved beyond in a feminist training program.

Another of the multi-leveled aspects of sexism which must be challenged in a feminist training program involves relationships among people. In feminist thinking, dichotomies between student and teacher, intern and supervisor, professional practitioner and academician, full professor and instructor, department chair and faculty member, and male and female are understood in the context of power relationships. In traditional settings, power is awarded to the people in the upper division of dichotomies in the hierarchies. Power in feminist thinking is not accorded by position; rather, influence is recognized for experience made publicly useful. Thus the relationships among the members of the training program are understood and handled in ways which are non-hierarchical, participatory and openly communicative. The goal is inclusion, not exclusion. Egalitarianism is the sought nature of relationships, not power.

The basic understanding of personality, mental illness, and assessment, diagnosis and treatment, in the dominant medical model of traditional mental health are still another level at which sexism must be understood. For example, atomistic views of personality and mental health, positing phenomena (personality, health) as composed of reduceable and distinct parts, a disease model, and empirical assumptions of measurement, prediction and control, cause and effect, stem from a rational arrogance which blindly presupposes limited postulations to be the total reality. The question of criterion in testing, diagnosis, and remediation is yet another example. The criterion question is essentially what is being used as a basis of judgement of what the norm is for the individual. Fundamentally, it is a normative issue. For example, the Minnesota Multiphasic Personality Inventory, a test often used in defining pathology in traditional mental health, was originally normed on institutionalized mid-western psychiatric patients. Since its origins and through continued development, the norming groups have expanded tremendously. Class, ethnicity and race, however, are not factors included in the interpretation by most professionals. The Rorschak, a projective personality test favored by mental health professionals of dynamic orientation, uses as a criterion the compiled judgement of white middle class professionals in Europe and America about which pathology is indicated by different verbal responses to ambiguous stimuli.

Diagnosis, based upon the Diagnostic and Statistical Manual, uses consensual professional judgement about symptoms associated or absent in differing pathologies. The traditional criteria for mental health are the absence of illness and conformity with socially defined appropriate behavior. The criterion for remediation efforts and views of effective personality development in the dominant model of mental health is lack of deviance from cultural norms, primarily as regard love and work. Love and work are seen in terms of dating or marriage, fulfilling contracts, and maintaining one's position in school or on the job.

Treatment efforts are aimed at controlling unusual symptoms and adjusting the individual to cultural norms. For instance, in day treatment facilities, the emphasis is on reinforcing patient continuation of medication, appropriate social skills, self-maintenance and work adjustment. The professional relationships within treatment efforts actively participate in establishing dichotomous hierarchical relationships. The privileged therapist is presented as knowing, right and powerful, while the patient is powerless and sick.

The traditional medical model, dominant in mental health, is thus in its very assumptions, structure and methods, both sharply limited to and reinforcing of the social norms. It is a strong force in maintaining the status quo. Indeed, some have argued with Szasz and Dumott that the chief function of traditional mental health is to control individuals who will not or cannot adjust to the lack of health required by the social norms. Feminist therapy programs must analyze the limits and weaknesses as well as the strengths of traditional mental health. Neither acceptance nor rejection can be considered a clear course of action. Rather, restricted views, limits and hidden arbitrariness must be articulated and different visions and practices developed. A feminist training program must be structured to allow and carried out to facilitate the development of new visions of personality and health, substantially different paradigmatic and theoretical assumptions, and systematic investigation of the effectiveness of alternative treatment efforts.

A feminist training program must attend to the many levels of sexism and feminist principles and non-sexist views of human nature, development and change. It must, as well, prepare its students to be practically and theoretically skilled in the dominant model. The latter is necessary for survival in the mental health arena. However, while dominant model competence is necessary and even useful, it is certainly not sufficient in itself nor without contradiction.

By definition, the main prerequisite for a feminist training program is an underlying structure of feminist principles and a profound understanding of sexism. Feminist ideology, instead of the traditional ideology, must define the goals, shape the process, and determine the content of the training program. The contradictions between the medical model's views and practices described here, and feminist views described in Chapter Three are stark. The medical model, quite simply, is not an appropriate framework through which to view the status and experience of women, and thus cannot adequately define the goals and methods of feminist therapy. Hence, people concerned with training feminist therapists face a dilemma: if they are to train therapists who will be competent to deal with the mental health problems of women, they must adopt nontraditional approaches and perspectives which might preclude their graduates from entering the mental health professions as now shaped by the professional associations. In order to ensure accreditation and the access of graduates to the mental health profession, the program must orient its training methods and approaches to two fundamentally different goals: Effective treatment of women, and dominant medical model standards for training programs.

In the remainder of this chapter, we will discuss a feminist training program in ideal terms; that is, we will discuss a hypothetical program whose structure, content and training methods are based purely upon the principles of feminism and on our knowledge of the psychology of women. At the same time we will be taking note of some of the practical obstacles which must be overcome if such a program is to be realized.

Basic feminist principles include a fundamental reliance on the experience of women, the belief that sexism is pervasive in this society, and responsible for many of the problems women face, and a consequent commitment to social action. Feminist therapy, based on these principles, attempts to put them into practice by developing research methods and modes of inquiry that incorporate various types and dimensions of women's experience. It adopts an interdisciplinary perspective and a pluralistic world view, inculcating a commitment to understanding the complexity of factors which affect the social context and status of women, and assumes a critical stance toward the assumptions and dogmas of traditional psychology.

It follows that a feminist training program must reflect in its structure, content and training methods the defining features of the psychology of women and, ultimately, the basic principles of feminism.

STRUCTURE

A major issue relating to the establishment of feminist training programs is whether it is realistic to attempt to develop them within a traditional academic context. We have seen how traditional training programs are fundamentally shaped by their context; and we have also seen how the feminist principles upon which feminist training programs are based inherently contradict many of the assumptions of traditional academia. The university setting is hierarchical, male dominated, controlled to a significant extent by external bodies, and allows for little student participation in basic decisions concerning its structure and content. On the other hand, as may be deduced from our discussion of feminist principles, and as will be spelled out in detail in the following sections, a feminist training program must by definition be nonhierarchical, committed to consensual participatory decision-making processes. It must also be critical rather than reflective of the assumptions and power dynamics inherent in the dominant social structures, including traditional mental health.

Perhaps in the freer economic, social and ideological climate of the late 1960s and early 1970s, universities might have had the flexibility to accomodate such a program. In the 1980s however, circum-

stances such as low budgets, increased faculty loads, stringent promotion and tenure policies, and an overall attitude of entrenchment,
self-protectiveness, and reluctance to change mitigate against the incorporation of a feminist training program into the university structure. It may very well be that the contradictions between the
philosophy, goals, content and structure of a feminist training program, and the assumptions, policies, and structure of the university
are simply too numerous and fundamental to be overcome. In that
case, establishing an independent feminist training program would
be preferable to making the compromises necessary to adapt a program to the university setting. That is, perhaps the only way a
feminist training program can develop and flourish without violating its underlying principles and the structure built on those principles is by the creation of independent organizations. These would be
similar to Gestalt and Psychoanalytical Institutes which have established themselves as intellectually respectable, effective training
centers without benefit of university sanction.

Another controversial issue relating to the structure of a feminist
training program is that of personnel policies. Some feminists contend that only women should be hired as trainers, teachers, advisors,
and supervisors, claiming the presence of men in what may be inter-
preted as power positions creates the appearance of patriarchy.
Moreover, in this view, men by definition have no personal experience of sexism, classism and racism against women, leaving them
with only a limited, secondhand knowledge. In addition, men cannot serve as role models of women who have effectively overcome
these realities, thus further restricting men's value as personnel in
feminist training programs.

While these objections are valid, there are strong arguments for
the view that the fundamental attributes of people hired to teach and
supervise in a feminist training program should be professional competence and a committment to feminism. While a sexist or incompe-
tent woman can do real harm to a feminist training program, a man
with feminist awareness and competence might be an asset. Also, a
program in which men as well as women serve as teachers more
closely reflects the real world than one employing only women, giving students an opportunity to learn to deal with men in a healthy,
open way, and to realize that men might be aware enough to change

and grow and move beyond their entrenched sexism.

Clearly, there is room for debate regarding the presence or absence of men in faculty and supervisory roles within a feminist training program. However, the central importance of fundamental sexist awareness, commitment to feminist principles, including egalitarian relationships in non-hierarchical structures, and academic and clinical competence, is not debatable.

Another issue relating to the structure and policies of the feminist training program is curriculum and its development. A feminist program would differ from traditional programs in many ways. One of these would be that suggestions for curriculum change could originate from any source, relevant to the program, students, field supervisors, developments in the psychology of women or the women's movement. Decisions about curricula changes would be made consensually, with the full participation of faculty, students, advisors, and field supervisors. The program, over time, would work out its own mechanisms to overcome cumbersomeness and abuse potential. Perhaps smaller representative groups, but representative of all and consensual in its decision-making, would become a basic procedure.

Similarly, the evaluation of faculty members would be a participatory process in which students and faculty members would engage in an open discussion of a teacher's strengths and weaknesses. This would be an assessment of the faculty member's contribution, or lack thereof, to the program and the field. This is done in the spirit of guiding her/him toward the continued development of awareness and skills.

Criteria for admitting new students would also differ from those of traditional programs. As we have seen, traditional programs select students on the basis of scores on standardized tests, grade point average, publication and, perhaps to a lesser degree, prior experience. A feminist training program would not ignore these criteria, but would employ them with a degree of skepticism and would adopt additional criteria reflecting the feminist belief in the validity and importance of many types of experience. While intellectual competence would certainly remain an important attribute of candidates for admission into the program, less reliance would be placed on the validity of test scores and other traditional measures as indicators of such competence than in a traditional program. The breadth of the feminist perspective enables feminist educators to recognize the race and class biases in standardized tests and the unreliability of grade point average as an indicator of the intellectual ability of a student who has followed a nontraditional course, or (if no allowance is made for subsequent grade inflation or the possible strengthening of professional motivation) of one whose undergraduate education occurred several years before. The feminist training program would supplement the somewhat unreliable admission criteria used in traditional programs with others which reflect a wide range of unique cultural, intellectual and personal qualities.

The selection process would attempt to assess the applicant's levels of personal, social, and cultural sensitivity and seek to admit people with a certain depth of self knowledge, combined with an awareness of others, a pluralistic view of reality, and a perception of the multi-leveled influence of sexism, racism, and classism. A further criterion for admission would be the nature and strength of the applicant's motivation. The selection process would attempt to determine which of the applicants wish to enter the program not out of naive idealism, but on the basis of a mature and knowledgeable desire to be involved in changing the social structure and psychological dynamics toward the end of improving women's lives. A specific mechanism for determining these criteria would need to be proposed and evaluated by the staff of the training program. They might include essays or creative demonstrations, intensive interviews, and group discussions, conversations with recommenders, and perhaps the use of attitude measures of sex-roles, discrimination based on racism, classism, ethnicity, and dogmatism. Also, admission decisions might have several stages, including a final decision after a student had experienced part of the program.

CURRICULUM

A fundamental difference between curriculum development in traditional and feminist therapist training programs is that while traditional programs reflect and perpetuate the norms and assumptions of the dominant social structures, an underlying intention of feminist programs is to foster a constructively critical attitude toward society. Since, as has been noted, the feminist orientation to mental health is founded on the conviction that most of the mental health problems of women result from the pervasively sexist nature of society, many of the courses included in the curriculum would focus on sexism in society as a whole and as it is reflected in the dominant assumptions of the mental health professions (i.e., the medical model), and as it affects the lives of all women, including female mental health clients and the trainees themselves.

Coupled with such an analysis would be an investigation of the ways this multi-leveled sexism could be combatted to improve the lives and thus the mental health of women. On one level would be an analysis of the phenomena of sexism, racism and classism as they occur throughout society. For example, an analysis would be made of sexism as it shapes the dominant social, political, economic and academic institutions, as well as the associated power dynamics, role expectations, and formal and informal means of reinforcing the status quo. This examination would extend to an analysis of the consequences of these conditions on the psychological, economic and social lives of women.

The following illustrative examples reflect the uniqueness required in feminist curricula:

One topic within this analysis would be the influence of the family unit (with its pressures, nurturing qualities, role expectations, and so on) on a woman's life. While some consideration would be given to such factors as traditional family therapy and traditional views of the family, the emphasis would be on the family as it shapes the lives of women.

A related topic would be children, considered not only in terms of developmental psychology, but also as they affect the lives of women in complex ways (e.g., social approval, the decision of whether or not to have children, the pressures of raising them and serving as a role model, and the restrictions that they place on women's choices).

Examples of other choices, all viewed in terms of the social influences that produced them and their subsequent effects on the experiences of women, are economic dependency, career issues, sexual harrassment and abuse, and retribution for non-traditional choices. These topics as well as others and their consequences would be coupled with discussions of how women can work toward the changes necessary to overcome political, economic, and social powerlessness, and achieve real choice and well-being.

This wide-ranging study of the social, political and economic contexts of women's lives and of the strategies designed to effect changes in those contexts would be accompanied by an intensive consideration of individual psychology as defined and shaped by the dominant forces. This consideration would entail both a detailed critical analysis of traditional mental health theory and practice and a discussion of mental health as seen from a feminist perspective. Sexism in the personality theory upon which many traditional mental health principles and practices rest would be considered, as would sexual bias in the research process, diagnosis, the etiology of pathology, and traditional ways of conceptualizing the psychological difficulties of women. The examination of sexism in traditional mental health theory would lead to discussion of sexism in traditional practice, e.g., clinical judgements, the uses of family therapy to reinforce stereotypes, the authoritarian nature of the therapeutic relationship, and the differential treatment of men and women.

The critical investigation of the underlying theoretical framework of the traditional mental health professions, as well as the practices and policies based on this framework, would lead to the development of modes of research and models of human nature, human interaction and mental health, which are based on or concomitant with feminist principles. For example, theoretical models such as learned helplessness, fear of failure and fear of success, and practical models of therapeutic interaction and social change would be presented from the feminist point of view. Further models, interventions and knowledge developed through feminist methods of research and investigation would become an active part of students' course work.

Because a feminist training program integrates political, social and economic considerations into its curriculum, the approach to the investigation and presentation of curricular areas must be interdisciplinary. *If* their assumptions and methods are critically analyzed from the feminist point of view, traditional disciplines can offer a valuable perspective on the forces shaping the lives of women, as well as the realities to be confronted in order to effect improvements in women's lives. Indeed, feminist scholars in these disciplines have already generated substantial critique of their traditional disciplines and analysis of the status of women. This knowledge must not be ignored in a feminist training program. Sociology, anthropology, history, political science, to name only a few, each contain ideas highly relevant to women's mental health. It is to feminist scholarship in these disciplines that mental health must look in order to understand the external factors shaping women's lives.

Related to the interdisciplinary perspective curricula, yet at a wholly different level, is a multi-paradigmatic epistomology. That is, within a feminist training program legitimacy would be accorded to a variety of ways of knowing. Because of the fundamental feminist principle positing a woman's experience as her reality base, the paradigmatic restraints of rational-empirical approach are expanded. In traditional training programs, only "knowledge" resulting from logical application of accepted theory or empirical results are accepted and sanctioned as legitimate. Epistomology and paradigmatic assumptions, as well as the politics of knowledge, would of necessity be the foci of a full discussion of alternative modes of knowledge. Indeed, treatment of these issues is exciting work in the forefront of diverse curret activity. Advocates of Tillich, Teillard DeChardin's work in the religious arena, Garfield in ethnographic research methodology, the members of The Sociology of Knowledge, Bertelenffy and more currently Sutherland in System Theory, Phenomenological Psychology developments most notably with the Duquesne group, Tart and Orrenstein working with Altered States of Consciousness, and Judith Christ in Women's Spirituality are all from different perspectives struggling with these issues.

It is, however, beyond the scope of this chapter to substantially address either their individual works or the issues uniting them. Suffice it to say that, in feminist training programs, while the rational-empirical modes of knowing would certainly exist, it would be only one of the many ways of knowing. Knowledge gained from research, analysis and investigation through diverse modes would be legitimized. Examples might include but not be limited to the following: the truths and experience portrayed in artistic expressions, as in some poetry, art, music and drama; the personal intuitive knowledge available to some people which is not reduceable to intellectual development and information access, social norms and cultural con-

ditioning; the knowledge, often inarticulated but nonetheless powerful, drawn from human experience; the knowledge of patterns, principles, or classically, forms, resulting from meditative activity, and
full connections with people, situations or events; the knowledge
gained through insight in various levels of consciousness characterized sometimes as religious, spiritual, cosmic, or transpersonal. The
point is that there exist many dimensions of knowledge and many
ways of knowing. Each have varying potential and limits. Because of
history, the dominance of the white male European mode, repeat-
ability, commonness and institutionalization, some are more developed and/or accepted (e.g., the Scientific Method), while others are
denied or discredited or severely limited and restricted (e.g., mysti-
cal experience is discredited, the truth in poetry is limited to poets
and restricted for the scientific, political, academic, or business
world).

Feminist training programs would not be uncritical of the very
real and imposed limits of non-traditional modes of knowing, nor
would truth be naively ascribed to outcomes of various dimensions
of knowing. To the contrary, rigorous investigation, analysis and development would be demanded. However, arbitrary imposition of
one mode of knowing, influencing the structure, and content and
process of "knowledge" would not be acceptable. Therefore curricula
sources, research methodologies and analytical processes would be
numerous and diverse. The rigorous development and use of many
sources, modes, and dimensions of knowledge would exist in
feminist training programs.

The emphasis on self-knowledge is centrally important. An over-
riding goal of feminist training programs would be to teach the student to heal. One important part would be learning how to further
examine herself and understand fully how she has been hurt by sexism, how she has adopted harmful adaptive patterns and how she
can heal herself and maintain her health. She must also understand
that her professional involvement in a traditional mental health field
will inevitably lead her, however unwittingly, to participate in sexism by acting as a bearer of the dominant social messages. On the
other hand, she must be equally aware of the costs to herself and her
clients of violating the social norms by advocating feminist positions
and practicing feminist principles.

The potential consequences to clients, as well as personal costs incurred by dealing as a feminist with various social structures and institutions, must be one issue covered in the discussion of community agencies. Discussion of community resources plays a more significant role in a feminist program than in a traditional training program. Agencies providing legal, economic, educational and social services (including the welfare, medical, and judicial systems) would be examined, as well as community resources for psychological, personal, and career development. Primary focus would be given to alternative structures for women, such as collectively-run women's centers and feminist services for divergent women's needs, for example addict programs, life planning with emphasis on employment, and of various types of support groups. The structures, purposes and services provided by these agencies would be discussed, as well as ways of referring clients to appropriate agencies, and to networking services. Importantly, not only would services for concrete needs be recognized, but also increased awareness, new ways of functioning and support-raised women's consciousness would be central to the discussion.

Agencies would not only be presented in terms of potential services to clients but analyzed in terms of their place within the larger social structure and the underlying power dynamics and internal pressures that force their clients to adjust to social norms.

For example, the welfare system, while apparently helping the unfortunate, forces women to live alone and withdraw from economic employment, and to accept her inability to support her children, in its eligibility requirements in the Aid to Dependent Children program. The assumption of her inability to financially support her children often confirms her view of self as a failure, when a more realist assessment would be the economic structure's discriminatory practices and the collaboration of the welfare system with that discrimination. Also, if one accepts A.D.C. payments, an agency case worker becomes involved. Though some case workers are able to avoid it, a major function is to police the eligibility requirements (no employment, no other adults living in the home, and no economic support from family, friends, fathers or other agencies) and to monitor the mother's child care practices. Through the enforcement of eligibility requirements and monitoring of child care practices, the woman is placed in a role which forces her into personal and economic dependency. She has been consigned to social, economic and personal powerlessness.

Students would be taught to initiate formal and informal strategies for combating sexism within agencies, to identify areas where agencies do not meet the needs of their clients, and to move toward creating services which do fill these needs. (For example, forcing policy changes in traditional agencies, planning ways in which an existing agency could aid in the creation of a women's center or in which an existing women's center could work to create welfare-funded, consciousness-raising groups, shared housing opportunities, or child care).

Since, as we have seen, the curriculum of a feminist training program would differ significantly in objectives and content from that of a traditional mental health training program, a fundamental question which must be considered when designing a feminist training program is the degree to which the traditional mental health curriculum would be included. Should the curriculum of a feminist program consist entirely of the specifically feminist subject areas as illustrated above, or should a consideration of these topics supplement and provide a feminist perspective on traditional curriculum areas? Currently, as might be expected, programs located within academic settings tend to add to traditional curricula a specific course or courses in women's counseling, while independent training programs would be more likely to adopt curricula consisting entirely of feminist oriented courses, often ignoring traditional areas.

As may be inferred from our discussion of specific curricula areas, we believe that many components of traditional training programs (communication skills, understandings of transference, pathology, learning, perception, development of theories, and such topics as career and stress) should be incorporated into the feminist training program with the proviso that each of these components be carefully examined for indications of sexist bias. That is, many traditional topics are essential to the training of a competent feminist therapist *if* they are placed within a feminist perspective and critically examined in terms of that perspective. Also, feminist therapists, if they are to professionally enter the field of mental health, must meet existing apprenticeship requirements in supervised experience, corpus of knowledge and procedure application. Existing programs have not yet accomplished this analytic integration goal. The Masters Counseling Program in Counseling Women at Boston University, for example, is comprised of a traditional counseling program with some courses and practical setting specific to women. While B.U. has developed a Counseling Women's program, laudable in its accomplishments, it has not yet developed an integrated feminist analysis. Even with its limits, indicative perhaps of the extent of the power of the controllers of the profession, the B.U. program is superior to the more typical accomodation of most departments, which is to either ignore totally or trivialize the issues and challenges by offering a course which focuses upon sex-roles.

Training programs outside of the university structure, as for example the program in New York City, while more advanced in feminist analysis, women's reality, and the development of helping skills, seems to lack thorough attention to the theory and practice of traditional mental health, the related academic disciplines and research, evaluation or other forms of systematic investigation.

Our position regarding the curricula of feminist training programs is that both traditional skills, theory, and research analyzed through a feminist critique, and specifically feminist subject areas should be present. The dominance of traditional mental health theory and practice controls entrance into the profession, thereby establishing membership which must be available for graduates of a feminist training program should they choose to seek it. Also, the content of traditional mental health both in theory and in some aspects of practice, is not justifiable when wholly reduced to politics. Indeed, the rich conceptual consideration of human functioning and demonstrated effectiveness in facilitating change of some strategies is important knowledge for competent therapists. If a feminist orientation is to have an impact on traditional theory, practice, research, and services in mental health, the critics and challengers must know its dominant language and forms. Its very dominance means that the traditional will be the focus of critique and challenge. Feminist therapy is not simply a reaction against traditional mental health but an alternative orientation. It must, however, contend with the historical, conceptual, developmental, and political power of traditional mental health.

Another basic question relating to the curriculum is whether the programs should attempt to inculcate a particular form of feminism (e.g., radical, socialist or reformist). We hold that since one of the basic tenets of feminism is the conviction that fundamental choices must be made on the basis of direct, individual experience, a training program based on feminist principles cannot legitimately seek to impose a particular model of feminism on its students, but should instead expose them to a wide range of differing perspectives, theories, and emphases within feminism, encouraging them to make intelligent, well-informed decisions about their own orientations. The curriculum discussed above includes areas directly related to all emphases of feminism. For example, a sophisticated analysis of sexism as it exists within various social structures and institutions exemplifies a socialist orientation. An examination only of sex roles and their impact on individual women represents a more reformist orientation. Allowing alternative modes of knowing reflects radical feminism. All the emphases, as shown in Chapter One, are integral to a feminist training program. The incorporation of these and others, e.g., separatist, third world, representing differing experience and analysis are essential if one of the goals of the training program is to provide a student with the opportunity to understand and the freedom to choose among the variety a view of feminism and style of therapy suited to her personality and individual experience. The choice must be made through knowledge of the full spectrum of available experience and analysis, not limited to data narrowed by acceptableness to current dominance.

TRAINING EXPERIENCE

Although the training sequence in a feminist training program would parallel traditional mental health training experience in many respects, there would be significant differences in emphasis. Prior to the graduated levels of learning clinical skills, the student would participate in consciousness-raising groups and individual counseling. The student would have defined herself as a woman and, in the context of women, have increased her awareness of the impact of sexism on her own and other women's development and status. She would also have developed a sophisticated comprehension of her self with all the strengths, weaknesses, and biases which are involved. Only after this step in education, comprised of several didactic courses and consciousness-raising, would the student undertake the sequential steps of clinical training. The sequence would be progressive in client contact and developmental in clinical skills, as in the traditional training programs.

The first step in the sequence would normally be a field work experience which focuses primarily on skill building in communication and therapeutic interaction. The practicum would be a closely supervised experience. The clients with which the trainee dealt would be carefully selected, and the field experience would often be preceded by role playing situations intended to simulate the therapeutic interaction.

The practicum would be followed by an internship during which the student is supervised and encounters a wider range of clients, as well as other activities, e.g., client advocacy, skill building, social or agency change efforts, and so on.

The feminist training experience would differ from traditional programs in several fundamental ways. First, the chosen supervisors would be feminists capable of establishing a nonauthoritarian relationship with the student and of guiding her in such activities as social analysis, client advocacy, developing new services, and resolving personal conflicts. Secondly, training sites would be selected with the full participation of the student. At least one of the sites selected for each student would be an agency having a feminist orientation and focused on the specific conerns and life experience of women, e.g., prevention programs for pregnant teens, women's centers, service for women of color, lesbian counseling centers. Third, each student would be required to thoroughly analyze the assumptions, goals, and social structure of the agency in which she is placed, as well as the value conflicts which may arise when she is placed as a client advocate in an agency which is to some degree anti-feminist in its structure, services, and client relationships. Fourth, the training sequence would include opportunities for the student to engage in experiences not found in traditional programs, such as community outreach, social change efforts, assertiveness training, and work with support and consciousness raising groups. Finally, the evaluation component of a feminist therapy program would differ from that of traditional training programs. Students being evaluated would be participants in the discussions among themselves, supervisors, faculty and agency staff. The emphasis would be on constructive criticism, aimed at developing the students' abilities and awareness, rather than solely judging performance. The criterion for evaluation would reflect a feminist view of mental health activities. Thus it would include the areas already mentioned above, as well as specific aspects of clinical skills and communication and relationships. There would be specific points of formal discussion and evaluation, but this evaluation process would also be ongoing in the individual supervision and class discussions. The separation that the traditional students feel between the placement site and academic courses would not be characteristic of this training program. Integration of these two sets of experience and analysis would flow from one to another. Academic course discussions would be based in part upon the experiences of practice, while discussions of practice would be based in part on feminist analysis and other course and life materials.

SUMMARY

In this long description of the structure, curriculum and training methods in a feminist training program, the characteristics based on feminist principles would be outlined succinctly as follows:

1. Sophisticated, intellectual analysis of social, political and economic forces in society through an interdisciplinary feminist perspective with emphasis upon sexism, racism and classism, with overt valving of pluralism.
2. Respect for the diversity of women's experience, and reliance on that experience for an understanding of the psychology and the development of effective ways of treating their mental health problems.
3. An emphasis on the self-development, expanded personal awareness, and self-healing of trainees.
4. A critical stance toward the basic (sexist) assumptions and struc-

tures of the traditional mental health professions and society as a whole.

5. Competent therapeutic understanding and skills.
6. A commitment to social action and the development of alternative social structures as a basic step toward improving the mental health of women.
7. A commitment to the development of new models of human nature and human interaction, and alternative analyses of the etiology and definition of pathology.
8. An attitude of self-criticism toward the program itself, i.e., an emphasis on an outgoing scrutiny of the power dynamics and subtle sexism occuring within the program's structure, curriculum, and training process.
9. An egalitarian, interactive process of decision making and evaluation in all basic areas of program structure, content and methods, as well as teachers and supervisors, and students' progress and performance.

We began this chapter with a review of similarities and structure of traditional mental health training programs and continued with a description of an ideal, contrasting feminist training program. There are two points which are vital in viewing this in perspective. First, our intent is not to "trash" traditional programs. We do not want to back away from the critique we have made, but we do want to acknowledge that many aspects of existing structure and curricula are important. For example, the sequence of clinical training, the extensive corpus of knowledge, and the concern for competence are all of value. Additionally, there are indeed a number of creative, well motivated people within traditional training programs.

Secondly, we described the feminist training program in the ideal. We have been free to do so since we have been creating in the abstract. The concrete implementation of such a program has yet to be begun. In this world, implementation means compromise. Compromises are difficult. Traditional programs have made and continue to make them. If feminist training programs are to be implemented, they too will have to compromise. It is our wish that the compromises of implementation will not undermine the feminist principles.

The aspects central to a feminist training program which must not be compromised are the centrality of women's experiences, the cooperative and collaborative rather than hierarchical functioning, the belief that no one is better or more right because of external characteristics which fit with dominant power systems, awareness of complex social forces which have shaped Western thought, concepts of human nature, mental health training and practices and the lives of women, and a feminist analysis which demands both an analytical framework and practices outside the press of the single vision of the dominant model.

Feminism must be understood as a process. It does have an analytical framework and implications for practices. While it offers principles, analysis and visions, it does not prescribe details of what changes should be made. It does hold the value of women, the rightness of choice among *real* alternatives, and the wrongness of convert power extended in social conditions, knowledge, and interpersonal actions. At its current stage of development, feminism critiques, informs, and offers; it does not prescribe ends. Understanding this process is central to the creation of a feminist training program in this chapter, as it will be in the next.

CHAPTER SEVEN

IMPACT ON TRADITIONAL MENTAL
HEALTH SERVICES

IN many ways, this final chapter, the impact on traditional mental
health, is a summary of the earlier chapters in the book. To analyze the impact of a feminist orientation to therapy on traditional
mental health services involves feminism, theory and practice, our
model of feminist therapy, training of mental health workers, and
notions of mental health and power systems. Indeed, to discuss any
one of these involves all of the others which is a convincing illustration of interactive phenomena. Feminism brings important insight
and analysis to conventional conceptualization and practice within
traditional mental health.

The discussions of feminism in the first and third chapters, con-
trasted with traditional mental health conceptualizations and practices reveal many differences. In summary, one is forced to conclude
that traditional mental health is in direct opposition to the principles
of feminism. It does not acknowledge oppression as a phenomenon
in women's and other non-dominant groups' experience. Nor does it
attempt to change oppression in social structures or theoretical beliefs or personal behavior. Thus it ignores its harmful impact on
women socially and psychologically. Also the custom-embedded yet
arbitrary rules of data organization and limited modes of analysis
function to exclude alternative ways of knowing, and women's experience.

Traditional mental health, even though used primarily by
women (Grove, 1980), has a male focus. Indeed, it has and does

participate in the value images and modes of functioning of power systems, thus violating the primary focus on women's experience, central to feminism. And with its male hierarchy and conservative power system reinforcing conventional theory and practice (limited role options, family adjustment to social norms, mother responsibility, sexist assumptions of female gender and misogynist theory and criteria), few could argue its anti-female orientation. Further, without exception the relationships are nonegalitarian. Whether viewing funding and policy making, interstaff or patient-therapist, relationships in mental health are hierarchical power relationships with little opportunity for participation in decision making. Traditional mental health services do not confront, nor rarely even consider social forces so intrinsically related to mental illness. Feminism's diverse analysis of harmful external forces and analysis of the causes of pathology (external forces made internal) is compelling. Even within conventional disciplines in mental health (community psychology/psychiatry and prevention proposed by Albee and promoted by the National Institute of Mental Health) and legislation (Community Mental Health Act, mandating Consultation and Education as a division of comprehensive mental health centers), voices are calling for expanded conceptualization and practice to confront external social forces. Yet one to one treatment of individual psychological disorders remain the predominant practice within traditional mental health.

If implemented, our model of feminist therapy would force changes in thinking, practices and services in traditional mental health. Our model's goals include changing social constraints (oppression and sexism in power systems, attitudes and structures, as well as socially pervasive discriminatory beliefs and practices) strengthening womens' agentry (awareness, analysis, responsibility and choice) and increasing skills (decoding, listening to one's own and other's voices, and developing interdependent support). These are not currently approached within traditional mental health. Rather, collusion with the power systems (value images, role option restrictions, mode of functioning, social control and rewards) is the outcome if not the intention of traditional mental health. The entire training chapter discussed ideological, content, process and structural changes necessitated by our model in training. Quite obviously many of them are the same when considering the impact on mental health services.

The conclusion that traditional mental health services are anti-feminist is inescapable. This chapter will analyze four broad areas of impact on traditional mental health services that will result from a feminist orientation to mental health: knowledge base change, institutional change, personnel change and ideological change.

One of the major impacts of a feminist orientation would be to broaden the knowledge base within mental health. Interdisciplinary perspectives, inclusive of both social constraints and research limits, must become fundamental in mental health conceptualizations and practice.

Women's history and women's studies, previously discussed, must also become an important broadener. The psychology of women, thoroughly integrated in academic curricula, licensing exams, and case conferences as well as journal publication and research grants, is yet another critical addition to the knowledge base. Validation of non-rational modes such as intuition, meditation and artistic/symbolic expression, perhaps more difficult, must also occur if current paradigmatic limits and epistemological prejudices are to be exposed and changed. These may be more difficult because unlike the interdisciplinary and women's perspective, these call for different ways of processing and different assumptions. Nonetheless, their inclusion is vital. It is most likely that through these non-rational modes, symbol, relationship, experience and connection, that women have drawn their strength to survive through lifetimes and centuries of oppression.

In the main, women have not been the creators of analytical forms which structure thought, control data, and shape ideology, though some have contributed through them. The unique strengths of women, enabling them to cope with devaluation, may in fact be outside the analytical structure, residing instead in other modes which are little understood and appreciated, as some radical feminists propose. If the mental health of women is to be understood, the value, function and existence of these dimensions must be · engaged.

Similarly, the knowledge base of mental health must come to include the experience of women and seek to understand its diversity.

Women's experience is at least threefold. It includes specific content such as violence against women, harrassment, abuse, rape, incest, psychosocial development within the context of discrimination by gender, physical and symbolic events such as menses, and potential pregnancy with its lifegiving strength. Women's experience also includes life lived with oppression, with all the gender ascription, devaluation, dependency and mixed messages. Women's experience also includes profound differences in orientation to self, interactions and values which the work of people such as Gilligan, Chodorow and Baker-Miller are beginning to uncover and articulate. Women's experience defined in these ways is different from men's experience, the focus of most conventional mental health conceptualization and criteria.

Women's experience becomes the data and criteria for mental health for women. The white, male, middle class experience is the data and criterion now. That must change to include both the experience of others and contradictions between them. Also, research and theory building must be expanded to include eclectic methodologies including those which listen directly to people's experiences, as discussed in earlier chapters.

If the knowledge bases were expanded in these ways, it would force the uncovering and correction of the currently dominated biases and control of "knowledge" in theory, research and practice extant in traditional mental health. It would also force the admission that current theories, models and research methods are simply thoughts, assumptions and ways of organizing information which arbitrarily reflect male experience, concerns and processes. Profound changes in theory would result if knowledge bases were expanded in accord with the feminist impact. One of these impacts will be fundamental recognition and challenge of both the limitedness and the arbitrariness in the content, structure, and process of traditional mental health knowledge. If this were changed: No longer would sound but nonempirical studies be rejected from traditional high status journals; no longer would the psychology of women be ignored or trivialized and shunted into an elective course; no longer would topics central to women's experience be unattended or judged as illegitimate; no longer would feminist scholars need to rework misogynist theories of the famous fathers (psychodynamic and object relations); no longer would women be judged and fit into the male (white and middle class, at that) criteria of mental health, which reinforces the dominant power systems; and no longer would social forces be ignored in consideration of and actions toward mental health.

Institutional changes would also be impacted by a feminist orientation. Services offered in mental health would be conceptualized and developed, evaluated, modified and continued on the basis of their demonstrated help to clients. Current standards in institutions of mental health are participant in power systems control. Tradition, custom, institutionalized professional practices, therapist preference, funding source (government or insurance company) policy, and cost effectiveness, are the standards upon which agency practices are based. They are not informed by demonstrated assistance to clients. For example, Blue Cross's five hundred dollar limit or typical Health Maintenance Organization's limits of ten sessions are based not on clients' needs, but on financial costs to the system. Intake procedures in agencies and initial sessions with private practice therapists are based upon agency and therapist considerations, not on clients' rights to participate in treatment decision, and certainly not on clients' free choice of therapist.

Feminism also calls for a change in the role and function of agency staff. To a large extent, traditional mental health is controlled by its professional function and conventional role. It is funded or authorized (licensed) by power systems to tend those persons damaged and rejected by social constraints. The feminist impact would demand roles and functions in the active pursuit of health, individually as well as socially focused. Therapists, aids, consulting psychiatrists, program counselors, and division coordinators would not carry out the current roles and functions of content experts treating the ills of individuals. Instead, they would become process consultants in their various positions. Agency staff or the private practitioner would no longer function in the expert role in the cause of mental illness. Nor would the role be that of manipulator, encourager and rewarder of conformance to acceptable social behavior. The feminist impact would require staff to work with clients and share information with them, regarding them as equals, who are in their *own* process of moving toward mental health.

One striking example is the use of formal (DSM:III) diagnosis determined solely by a therapist and confirmed, if at all, by agency staff and the consulting psychiatrist. Formal diagnosis excludes the client from participation and often even knowledge of their cases. This is typically routine procedure for all clients, regardless of their competence and degree of pathology. The diagnosis categories, critiqued earlier, and the language of diagnosis are exclusionary labeling and are directly related to the kind, method, and goal of the therapeutic procedures used. The client is cast into the position of object, to whom things are done, for her own good.

These views, roles, and functions of traditional mental health are described more fully in Chapters Two and Five. In short, the feminist impact would require the staff to be process consultants. This is an important distinction from content expert, articulated in the organizational behavior and particularly organizational development literature and one demanded by feminism.

The feminist impact would change the functions, roles, activities, selection and committment of administrators as well. In essence, the hierarchy would be dissolved. Administrators would function to facilitate the goals and functioning of the staff and clients. This might mean carrying out maintenance functions such as getting funding, securing new staff or setting up in-service training. It also might involve community work to establish new support services. It might involve working with other agencies in effort to change their practices and policies which run counter to mental health, e.g., legal systems or hospital policies. Advocacy for an individual client along with advocacy against harmful social conditions would be of prime import. Working toward social change (e.g., working to change state or federal requirements inconsistent with client based service and mental health) might also be involved. Administrators would also report current issues within the mental health bureaucracy to the staff, for mutual consideration and action decisions. The administrators would function not as bosses and policy makers, but as participants with the staff and as helpers of clients moving toward mental health. The administrators would serve at the will of the staff, not the board of directors. These structural and functional changes are consistent with and necessary for egalitarian instead of power relationships within the institution.

Yet another institutional change in mental health, brought through the application of a feminist orientation, would be policy change and functional commitment to the assumptions in the Harmful Adaptation chapter. Particularly, there must be therapeutic intervention (change) aimed at the environment in which women live, if their mental health is to be achieved and maintained. While individual therapy would not end, considerable effort would be directed toward challenging and changing the social constraints in women's environments. Tied in with our earlier discussion of harmful adaptation, corrective action and health maintenance as well as with Albee's (1981) and others' notions of prevention and the Comprehensive Mental Health Act's Consultation and Education, the priorities of mental health would be altered. Returning the patient to effective coping and adjusting to social norms would not be the goal. The priorities would become: advocacy for social change, change in the political process, confrontation with harmful policies, education in the community and overt political stands for individual mental health workers and agencies at local, state and federal levels. The voice of mental health professionals would be added to those who speak for mental health development and against harmful images, roles, options, norms and institutional functioning. Another commitment would be to the creation of the structures and services which help women: effective day care, self help groups, women's centers, collaborative living situations, programs affirming the strengths of women and raising their consciousness. In short, nonoppressive social conditions and growth enhancing activities would be developed or supported by mental health professionals.

Also, modes of functioning and agency practices in therapy and policies which endorse egalitarian participation and negate hierarchy would be developed and become the operating procedure were a feminist impact felt. This would span the activities from policy making, intern training, and evaluation to individual therapy, records and group leadership. For example, mental health workers would actively support, encourage or develop groups based upon the experiences and needs of women. A number of these groups might be self-help groups which would not involve professional mental health workers. Though in establishing the groups or on a group requested bases, the professional mental health workers might share their knowledge and skill in group process, effective communication, goal setting, norm establishment, or conflict resolution. But women in the group would function autonomously, asking for specific resources if they experience the need for it.

Similarly, individual therapists or agency staff might head a group whose aim would be to ready women who have been more severely damaged or are further from their own voices. However, the groups would function in shared leadership and training models, not as experts treating patients. The underlying belief is that women's experience is central and that women can and have been helpful to themselves and each other. This should be acknowledged and validated. Enabling women's mental health, functioning as a requested process consultant and commitment to changing social constraints are important feminist impacts which force a different view and method of therapy.

A feminist impact on mental health services and its practitioners would require a consistent re-examination of relationships and beliefs. Traditional forms of service would need to be screened against inappropriateness. Some of the old ways would indeed be found useful, particularly for the severely harmed. Mental health has accomplished a great deal in severe pathology and a variety of intervention strategies. However, continual monitoring of procedures, practices and methods for bias and collaboration with oppression and harmful social reinforcement must become the standard. Certainly with exceptions, goals and methods of therapy, ideas of therapy and case work, relationships in therapy, diagnosis and labeling functions in the service of mental illness and value as well as world view limits must be challenged and changed. Also, the person of the therapist must be questioned. Their values, beliefs and process must be examined. Hard questions need to be raised and answered. The ability of the therapist to listen and understand a client's experience, particularly when it differs from their own (for example, lesbians, nontraditional roles, incest, collective living, race, class, culture) is only one critical question. Another is the therapists' ideological, theory and attitudinal assumptions as well as their process of interaction with clients. Can therapists who are sexist and hierarchical in their lives outside of therapy, truly not be in therapy? Yet another related question is: Where are they in their own mental health and commitment to women's and social change?

These institutional and therapeutic changes are illustrative of the many which would be brought by the impact of a feminist orientation. Were this impact to occur, mental health services would no longer perpetuate the power system's oppression of women seeking their adjustment to social constraints. Instead, mental health services would become forces committed to undoing damage, achieving and maintaining health.

A feminist orientation would also impact on the personnel in mental health professions. The changes in role and function would require different personnel in traditional mental health services or a differently oriented private practitioner. Hiring, retention, in service training and consultations, as well as policy affecting job descriptions, staff evaluations and documentation would all change to reflect feminist mental health goals, egalitarian relationships and participant decision making structures. Further, personnel would reflect and be committed to broader knowledge bases than the traditional professional, and expertise in social change and understanding of oppression with its social constraints and psychic effects on women would be fundamental. The broader knowledge base has already been discussed in this and other chapters. The expertise in social change would include a thorough understanding as well as skill in prevention, organizational development and the political process.

Sophisticated knowledge of oppression and its social and psychic effects would include the real comprehension of its damaging impact on women, nonconformists, nondominant groups, the differently aged, abilitied, colored, and cultured.

Personnel within the feminist context would need to develop new and expand existing skills. Listening skills in hearing individual and community experience and needs are one part. Skills in developing services and information to address the social and psychological needs of the oppressed and to enable them to pursue their own mental health are another part of the needed skills. And skills to analyze, strategize and survive with feminist oriented services in the context of hostile power systems are yet additional needed skills.

These changes would require redefined roles of mental health professions and they clearly involve different orientations, knowledge and skills. Planners and agents of social change, as well as individual enablers, are the essential differences, and this rests upon differing beliefs and values. Changed ideology, which places mental health in opposition to the power systems no longer tending their damaged and rejected, no longer accepting their norms and criteria, is basic to the feminist impact on traditional mental health.

The impact of feminism on the ideology of traditional mental health is profound. In strong part, it is what this book has been about. Briefly, several changes are identified below. As previously discussed, feminism would require an orientation and committment to:

1) A reconceptualization of health and its promotion, both socially through social change and individually through enabling the pursuit of mental health. Adjustment to social norms or naive individual responsibility are uncovered as harmful and inadequate beliefs. 2) A belief in and value of pluralism which recognizes human differences, affirms them and works toward their social and individual validation. 3) An articulation of external forces and their impact which is often harmful to mental health. The dichotomization of mental health. The dichotomization of mental and social forces must be uncovered and seen for its power system reinforcement. 4) A reorientation to women's experience, not their constrained roles and social expectations, must become the appropriate professional criterion, central in thinking judgement and action. 5) A commitment to a feminist orientation to therapy and services must become the fundamental method including shared information and analysis with clients rather than the traditional exclusive and excluding professional knowledge and expert stance. This would also include changes in access and control dynamics in therapy, within the agency and in the social arena. 6) A commitment to roles and functions of change agents, thus challenging agency policy, interagency practice and social constraints as they delimit women's possibilities or undermine access, participation and egalitarian relationships. 7) An involvement in the political process, in funding requirements, in the professions, in other services impacting on women, and in the local community through education and action. 8) A view of mental health services changed from that of controlling the nonconforming in challenging and changing the power system images, values and

structures which are causative to mental illness.

Traditional mental health must become *health services* which actively work to change the forces which cause illness in clients, agencies, and communities. The basic and fundamental beliefs of feminism force actions policies, roles, functions and limited knowledge of traditional mental health to be contested, and force engagement in the process of developing new conceptualizations, processes and practices. This process is barely begun, but sorely needed. Feminism has the analysis and points the direction, but has not the answers. The feminist challenge is a demand to think anew about mental health and to act for necessary conditions, structures, skills and goals for its achievement and maintenance.

We urge mental health workers to challenge the traditions, power structures, theory, training and practice which maintains the status quo in collusion with social constraints and oppression on women.

We are not making a polite request of traditional mental health; we are challenging and demanding change. If it does not change, then mental health will continue to damage women and continue to be a part of the hostile environment. Traditional mental health can no longer hide from its complicity in women's mental illness. If traditional mental health does not address these needed changes, then it can no longer avoid the responsibility for the human consequences of its collusion and reinforcement of sexist norms and values.

BIBLIOGRAPHY

1. Albee, G.: The prevention of sexism. *Professional Psychologist, 12*:20-28,1981.
2. Argyris, C.: *Intervention Theory and Method.* Reading, Addison-Wesley, 1970.
3. Arieti, S.: *Creativity: The Magic Synthesis.* New York, Basic, 1976.
4. Ascher, Carol: *Simone DeBeauvoir, A Life of Freedom.* Boston, Beacon, 1981.
5. Baker-Miller, Jean: *Toward a New Psychology of Women.* Boston, Beacon, 1981.
6. Bardwick, J.M.: *Psychology of Women: A Study of Biocultural Conflicts.* New York, Harper, 1971.
7. Bertalanffy, L.V.: The history and status of general systems theory, in Klir, George (Ed.): *Trends in General Systems Theory,* New York, Wiley, 1972.
8. Brodsky, A.: Consciousness-raising group as a model for the therapy with women. *Psychotherapy: Theory, Research and Practice, 10*:24-29,1973.
9. Brodsky, A.: Is there a feminist therapy? Paper presented at a symposium, Issues in Feminist Therapy, Southeast Psychological Association, Atlanta, March 1975.
10. Broverman, I., Broverman, D., Clarkson, F., Krantz, P., & Vegel, S.: Sex-role stereotyping and clinical judgements of mental health. *Journal of Consulting and Clinical Psychology, 34 (1)*:1-7, 1970.
11. Carlson, R.: Understanding women: Implications for personality theory and research. *Journal of Social Issues, 28*:17-32, 1972.
12. Carter, D., & Rawlings, E. (Eds.): *Psychotherapy for Women.* Springfield, Thomas, 1977.
13. Chesler, P.: *Women and Madness.* Garden City, Doubleday, 1972.
14. Cox, S.: *Female Psychology,* The Emerging Self, 2nd ed., New York, St. Martin's, 1981.
15. Chodorow, N.: *The Reproduction of Mothering.* Berkeley, UC Press, 1978.
16. Christ, J.: *Diving Deep and Surfacing.* Boston, Beacon, 1980.
17. David, S.P.: Feminist therapy: No lunatic fringe. *The New Women's Times, 1(3)*: 3, 1980.
18. DeChardin: *Phenomenological Man.* New York, Harper, 1961.
19. Dinnerstein, P.: *The Mermaid and the Minotaur.* New York, Harper, 1977.
20. Fishel, A.: What is a feminist therapist?, *Ms.,* June, 1979.
21. Foxley, C.: *Non-Sexist Counseling.* Dubuque, Kendall/Hunt, 1978.

22. Franks, V., & Burtle, V. (Eds.): *Women in Therapy.* New York, Brunner/ Mazel, 1974.
23. Freeman, J. (Ed.): *Women: A Feminist Perspective.* Palo Alto, Mayfield, 1974.
24. Frye, Marilyn: *The Politics of Reality: Essays in Feminist Theory.* Trumansburg, Crossing, 1983.
25. Garfinkel, H.: *Studies in Ethnomethodology.* Englewood Cliffs, Prentice Hall, 1967.
26. Gilbert, L.: Feminist therapy. In Brodsky, A. & Hare-Mustin, R.: *Women and Psychotherapy.* New York, Guilford, 245-265,1980.
27. Gilligan, C.: *In a Different Voice.* Cambridge, Harvard, 1982.
28. Grady, K.E.: Sex bias in research design, *Psychology of Women Quarterly, 5:*628-636,1981.
29. Greenspan, M.: *A New Approach to Women and Therapy.* New York, McGraw-Hill, 1983.
30. Griffith, A.: Feminist counseling: A perspective. In Smith, D.E., and David, S.J. (Eds.) *Women Look at Psychiatry.* Vancouver, Press Gang, 149-154,1975.
31. Grove, W.: Mental illness and psychiatric treatment among women, *Psychology of Women Quarterly,* Spring, 1980.
32. Hare-Mustin, R.: An appraisal of the relationship between women and psychotherapy: 80 years after the case of Dora, *American Psychologist, 38(5),* May, 1983.
33. Hare-Mustin, R.: Feminist approach to family therapy, *Family Process, 17:*181-193, June, 1978.
34. Heriot, J.: The double bind: healing the split, in Robbins, J.H. and Siegel, R.J. (Eds.): Women Changing Therapy, New Assessments, *Values and Strategies in Feminist Therapy.* New York, Haworth, 1983.
35. Holroyd, J., and Brodsky, A.: Psychologists' attitudes and practices regarding erotic and nonerotic physical contact with patients, *American Psychologist, 34:*843-849, 1977.
36. Hurney, K.: *Feminine Psychology,* New York, Norton, 1967.
37. Hyde, J.S. and Rosenberg, B.G.: *Half the Human Experience,* 2nd ed., Lexington, D.C. Health, 1980.
38. Jaggar, A.: Political philosophies of women's liberation, in Vettepling-Braggin, M., Ellison, F., and English, J. (Eds.): *Feminism and Philosophy,* Totowa, Littlefield, Adams, 1977.
39. Janeway, Elizabeth: *Powers of the Weak.* New York, Knopf, 1980.
40. Kaplan, Marcie: A woman's view of DSM III, *American Psychologist, 38(7),* July, 1983.
41. Kaplan, A.G., and Sedney, M.A.: *Psychology and Sex Roles, An Androgynous Perspective.* Boston, Little, Brown, 1980.
42. Kaplan, A., Brooks, B., McComb, A., Shapiro, E., and Sodano, A.: Women and Anger in Psychotherapy, in Robbins, J.H. and Siegel, R.J. (Eds.): *Women Changing Therapy: New Assessments, Values, and Strategies in Feminist Therapy.* New York, Haworth, 1983.

43. Kell, B., & Mueller, W.: *Impact and Change: A Study of Counseling Relationships.* Englewood Cliffs, Prentice-Hall, 1966.

44. Kirk, S.: The role of politics in feminist counseling, in Robbins, J.H., and Siegel, R.J. (Eds.): *Women Changing Therapy: New Assessments, Values and Strategies in Feminist Therapy.* New York, Haworth, 1983.

45. Kronsky, B.: Feminism and psychotherapy, *Journal of Contemporary Psychotherapy, 3(2):*89-98.

46. Langland, E., and Grove, W. (Eds.): *A Feminist Perspective in the Academy.* Chicago, University of Chicago, 1983.

47. Lerman, H.: What happens in feminist therapy? In Cox, S. (Ed.): *Female Psychology: The Emerging Self.* Chicago, Science Research, 1976.

48. McHugh, M., Koeske, R.D., and Frieze, I.H.: *Guidelines for Non-Sexist Research,* Division 35 Task Force, December, 1981.

49. Miller, Jean Baker, see Baker-Miller.

50. Mitchell, J.: *Women's Estate.* New York, Vintage, 1973.

51. Moskol, M.: Feminist theory and casework practice, *Social Work, 22(6):* 447-454, November, 1977.

52. O'Leary, V.E.: Feminist research: Problems and prospects. *Psychology of Women Quarterly, 5:*645-653, 1981.

53. Orrenstein, Robert: *The Psychology of Consciousness.* New York, Viking, 1972.

54. Robbins, J.H., and Siegel, R.J.: *Women Changing Therapy.* New York, Haworth, 1983.

55. Rush, A., & Mander, A.: *Feminism as Therapy.* Berkeley, Bookworks, 1974.

56. Schaef, A.W.: *Women's Reality.* Minneapolis, Winston, 1981.

57. Schaffer, K.: *Sex-Role Issues in Mental Health.* Reading, Addison-Wesley, 1980.

58. Seiden, A.: Overview: Research on the psychology of women: II: Women in families, work, and psychotherapy, *The American Journal of Psychiatry, 133(10):*1111-1112, October, 1976.

59. Shepard, H.: Explorations in observant participation, in Bradford, L.P. Gibb, J.R., and Benne, K.D. (Eds.): *T-Group Theory and Laboratory Method: Innovation in Re-education.* New York, Wiley, 379-394,1964.

60. Smith, D., and David, S. (Eds.): *Women Look at Psychiatry.* Vancouver, Press Gang, 1975.

61. Stanley, L. & Wise, S.: Breaking Out: *Feminist Consciousness and Feminist Research,* Boston, Rutledge, 1983.

62. Sturdivant, S.: Therapy with women. Springer Series: *Focus on Women,* Volume Two, New York, Springer, 1980.

63. Sutherland, Donald: *General Systems Theory for the Social Sciences.* New York, Braziller, 1973.

64. Tart, Charles: *States of Consciousness,* New York, Dutton, 1975.

65. Task Force on Sex Bias and Sex Role Stereotyping in Psychotherapeutic Practice: Guidelines for therapy with women, *American Psychologist,* December, 1978.

66. Tennov, D.: Feminism, psychotherapy and professionalism. *Journal of Contemporary Psychotherapy, 5:* 106-116, 1973.

67. Tillich, Paul: *The Courage To Be.* New Haven, Yale, 1952.
68. Unger, R.K., Through the Looking Glass: No Wonderland Yet! *Psychology of Women Quarterly, 8(1):*9-32, 1983.
69. Wallston, B.S.: What are the Questions in Psychology of Women? A Feminist Approach to Research, Presidential address for Division 35 presented at the annual meeting of the American Psychological Association, 1979.
70. Weisstein, N.: Kinde, kuche, kirche as scientific law: Psychology constructs the female, in Morgan, R. (Ed.): *Sisterhood is Powerful.* New York, Vintage, 1970.
71. Weitzman, Lenore: *Sex Role Socialization.* Palo Alto, Mayfield, 1979.
72. Wesley, C.: The women's movement and psychotherapy, *Social Work,* 120-124, March, 1975.
73. Williams, E.: *Notes from a Feminist Therapist.* New York, Dell, 1976.
74. Williams, J. (Ed.): *Psychology of Women's Selected Readings.* New York, Norton, 1979.
75. Worell, J.: New directions in counseling women. *The Personnel and Guidance Journal, 58(7):*477-484,March, 1980.
76. Wycoff, H.: Radical psychiatry for women, in Carter, D. & Rawlings, E. (Eds.): *Psychotherapy for Women.* Springfield, Thomas, 1977.

INDEX

D

Daley, Mary, 21
Darwin, Charles, 15
David, S.P., 52
deBeauvoir, Simone (*see* Beauvoir, Simone de)
DeChardin, 151
Democratic Party, 4
Dependence, 42
Dichotomization, 85, 86
Dichotomous conceptualizations, 64
Dinnerstein, P., 56, 63
Dix, 133
Douglas, Frederick North, 4
DSM III, 56

E

Egalitarianism, 61
Elliot, George, 17
Engels, Frederick, 10
English Women's Journal, 9
Equal Rights Amendment (ERA), 20, 36, 47
Existential approaches, 73
Expression, 123-124

F

Fawcett, Millicent Garrett, 7
Feminism (*see* specific headings)
Feminist therapy, outline of, 22-44
Feminist therapy, limits of, 43-44
Feminist Training Program, 140
Fishel, A., 27
Freeman, J., 35, 46
Freidan, Betty, 21

G

Garfield, 151
Garrison, William Lloyd, 4
Geddes, Patrick, 15-16
Germany, 10-13
Gestalt therapy, 73, 102, 146
Gilbert, L., 27, 30, 41
Gilligan, C., 37, 51, 52, 54, 56, 63, 164
Goldman, Emma, 18
Goodwin, William, 17
Gottschalk, 54
Grady, K.E., 54
Greenspan, M., 27, 28, 36, 37, 51

Griffith, A., 25
Grimke, Angelica and Sarah, 4
Group dynamics, 125
Grove, W., 52, 161

H

Harmful adaptation, definition of, 69
Hare-Mustin, R., 27, 50
Harvard Lab in Community Psychiatry, 138
Health maintenance, 119
Health Maintenance Organization, 165
Herman, 51
History of feminism, 3-21
Horner, 63
Human Potential Movement, 63

I

Identification, 126-127
Inculcation, 83
Independence, 42
Interdependence, 42

J

Janeway, E., 63, 89, 120
Johnson, 54
Juchaz, Marie, 12

K

Kaplan, A.G., 88, 95
Kell, B., 39
Kerrenza, 17
Krantz, 29

L

Labor, division of, 47
Lange, 132
Lerman, 36, 37, 39, 40
Lesbian feminism, 21
Liberal
  feminism, 4, 13, 35, 36, 46, 47, 70, 88
  Party, 7
Liberalism, definition of, 3

M

Male aggression, positive valuing of, 84
Mander, 25, 37
Marx, Karl, 9, 10
Mill, John Stuart, 6, 17